KING ARTHUR AND HIS KNIGHTS

RIVERSIDE EDITIONS

RIVERSIDE EDITIONS

UNDER THE GENERAL EDITORSHIP OF

Gordon N. Ray

KING ARTHUR
AND HIS KNIGHTS

Selections from the Works of

Sir Thomas Malory

EDITED WITH AN INTRODUCTION AND NOTES BY

EUGÈNE VINAVER

HOUGHTON MIFFLIN COMPANY

Boston · The Riverside Press Cambridge

CONTENTS

INTRODUCTION

by Eugène Vinaver

In the London *Observer* of 25 October 1953 Mr. Lionel Hale described in the following terms his impressions of a broadcast of Malory's *Quest of the Holy Grail:*

> "But this is going to pall, this is going to start becoming tedious!" I said to myself at about 9.30 p.m. on Tuesday, after ten minutes of the *Quest of the Holy Grail* adapted by Mr. Douglas Cleverdon from Malory. Yet 11 p.m. found me still listening, and indeed coming back to the surroundings of a drawing-room with a start of surprise. Such knights, such ladies in distress, such single combats, such ships in samite, such fiends, such vows — the chivalry went briskly by, with their own beauty and their own simplicity of bravura, and never even relapsed into a dog-trot.
>
> My groundless fears were of the method — the use of spoken narration, with short interspersed dramatic dialogue. Surely, I thought, the narrator must begin to sound intrusive: surely not even Mr. Deryck Guyler as Gawayne or Mr. Robert Harris as Lancelot can make anything of such fleeting and fugitive appearances. Wrong: one settled easily into the formula. Much was due, I thought, to the tact and variety with which that impeccable air-voice of Mr. Norman Shelley read the narration. But really the triumph was Malory's. What tales, and what a teller!

Very little is known of the author of these tales. A knight, an adventurer and a soldier, he was born in the early years of the fifteenth century and died on 14 March 1471, having spent much of the last twenty years of his life in prison. It was there that he wrote most, if not all, of his works, completing the last one in 1469 or early in 1470. Fifteen years later, on 31

July 1485, William Caxton published the entire collection
in one volume entitled *Le Morte Darthur* which has since
become the fountainhead of English Arthurian fiction. With
the possible exception of *The Canterbury Tales,* no English
book bequeathed to us by the Middle Ages has to the same
degree caught the imagination of modern readers. And yet,
when one asks oneself how this came about, how the obscure fif-
teenth-century 'knight-prisoner' achieved his lasting triumph,
the answer is not easy to find. What he did was to 'reduce into
English,' as Caxton puts it, certain French prose romances of
the thirteenth century. Outwardly, apart from the 'reduction,'
his work did not differ much from its French prototypes. But
while the modern reprints of Malory's Arthurian tales rival in
number those of the great English classics, while English listen-
ers to-day find delight in his 'knights, ladies in distress, single
combats and ships in samite,' Malory's 'French books' as he calls
them have long since lost their appeal and not a single trace of
their once powerful influence remains in modern French poetry
and fiction. They have not even been condemned, as great
literature often is, in the name of newly fashioned doctrines,
but simply forgotten as though they had never existed. English
criticism may occasionally have been severe to Malory. Even
such a devout Malory scholar as E. K. Chambers felt obliged
to make some reservations. He was perturbed by the
'overgrowth of chivalric adventures,' by Malory's failure to
maintain certain characters 'on the same plane throughout,' by
his apparent inability to tell completely 'two of the world's
dozen great love stories' — that of Tristan and Iseult and that
of Lancelot and Guinevere. 'Through much of it,' he wrote,
'we walk perplexedly.' But fortunately such perplexities never
hinder the suspension of disbelief except in the critic's own
mind; and much as Malory's readers may have been puzzled by
his incoherences, they have never on that account ceased to
experience the fascination of his narrative.

Wherein this fascination lies is for each reader to determine
for himself: all 'definiteness' in this field, as Valéry reminded us
not long ago, 'remains subjective.' But one aspect of the problem might perhaps be clarified without detriment to individual
judgment, namely, Malory's method of dealing with the
peculiarities of early French fiction. It is customary to say

that any medieval French romance of chivalry is — the phrase is George Saintsbury's — 'a vast assemblage of stories,' a collection of heterogeneous tales put together without any sequence or logic, incoherent, often absurd, and calculated to confuse even the most careful reader. More than three centuries ago one of Don Quixote's friends expressed surprise that 'more people did not go mad when they read such books'; for they were composed, he thought, 'in such a way that no reader could find his way about them.' And because it is as difficult for us to-day as it was for late sixteenth-century readers to discern any design or method behind the complete texture of these vast and unwieldy volumes, we conclude that they are devoid of such things altogether and should be written off as an unfortunate accident in the literary history of Europe. Recent research has shown, however, how rash this condemnation is, and how important the aesthetic principle underlying the structure of the works which Malory used as his models. One of his main sources was the French Arthurian Prose Cycle — the 'Vulgate' Cycle as it is usually called nowadays — composed in the first half of the thirteenth century, probably between 1225 and 1230. It contained three main elements: the courtly stories dealing with Lancelot's adventurous life; the chronicle stories concerned with the history of Arthur's kingdom; and the Grail stories which introduced into the realm of romance the mystical aspirations of the knights engaged in a holy quest. The central portion of the cycle was the romance of Lancelot, the longest of all; on either side of it were two other branches: a Grail branch and a chronicle at one end — the *History of the Grail* and the *Merlin* — and a Grail branch and a chronicle at the other — the *Quest of the Holy Grail* and the *Death of Arthur*. The cycle as a whole is certainly vast, so vast that no complete critical edition of it has yet been attempted, but it did not grow up by process of a mere accumulation of narrative material. In most cases, when a 'branch' or an incident was added, the purpose of the addition was to elucidate or to anticipate stories which were already in existence. Thus, the *History of the Grail* which was the last of the branches to be produced was placed first in the final arrangement because its purpose was to prepare the ground for an earlier branch, the *Quest of the Holy Grail*. This 'backward' growth of the narrative implies a method still clearly distinguishable in the work of Rabelais, who began with the adventures of Pantagruel and then went on to the life story of Pantagruel's father, Gargantua: a modern novelist would probably have written his *Gargantua* first. The same process can be observed in such early forms of imaginative narrative as the French epic poems of the twelfth century, many of which were written to commemorate the early life or the lives of the parents and ancestors of a hero whose deeds were already on record.

It stands to reason that if a story or a set of stories is to be added as a preliminary to an already existing sequence of themes, and each of these lengthened 'backwards' simultaneously with the others, the result can only be a very complex pattern of themes alternating one with another like the strands of a woven fabric. There can be no steady progression of a single theme from the beginning to the middle and from the middle to the end, such as we are accustomed to find in a work of fiction composed in accordance with our modern idea of coherence. The beginning is no longer, according to Aristotle's definition, 'that before which there is nothing' or the end that which calls for no continuation. On the wide and constantly expanding canvas of a cycle of romances there is always room for a further lengthening of any one of the carefully interwoven threads. Nothing is more alien to our idea of 'structure' than this remarkable structural achievement. It represents in the field of fiction a sense of shape which is the very opposite of our cherished notion of 'beginning, middle, and end,' the negation of our well-established formal values; and the impact of the romances of chivalry on Don Quixote's mind is perhaps nothing more than the extreme form of the bewilderment experienced by any modern reader in face of these strange compositions.

Had Malory lived a hundred years later his reaction might have been similar to Don Quixote's; but he was sufficiently close to the tradition of early French romances to understand their elusive mechanism, and yet sufficiently independent of that tradition to be able to discover the means by which they could be adapted to a new conception of narrative. Mere condensation, such as many adaptors have practised before and since, was clearly not enough. The entire fabric of the text had to be unravelled and each thread, as far as possible, separated from the others. This involved the use of two different techniques. Certain stories, reproduced with minor modifications, could be made self-contained by being simply detached from their context. *Lancelot and Elaine* and *The Knight of the Cart* are examples of this relatively easy process. In the manuscript of the French prose *Tristan* which Malory used for his *Lancelot and Elaine* the story served as an introduction to an expanded version of the Grail quest, the 'third book' of the *Tristan*. Malory's story has no such sequel; it stands all by itself and, Malory tells us, there is 'no rehearsal of the third book.' The incidents which form the basis of Malory's *Knight of the Cart* originally occurred half-way through the prose *Lancelot*, long before the Grail adventures began; they were part of a complex sequence of themes and their place in the sequence was essential to their meaning and purpose. Yet such is Malory's indifference to this delicate arrangement that he inserts his *Knight of the Cart* among the incidents supposed to have taken place some time after the completion of the Grail quest. The other method is more elaborate. It consists in building a continuous narrative upon the frail structure of fragments scattered over wide stretches of the French cycle. One of Malory's early works, *The Noble Tale of Sir Lancelot*, consists of three such fragments. By carefully selecting them and bringing them together he gives his *Tale* perfect continuity and, by modern standards, a degree of coherence which its component elements never possessed. In his later writings such as *The Poisoned Apple* and *The Fair Maid of Astolat* his use of this technique shows still greater subtlety and skill. In the French romance — the *Mort Artu* — from which he borrowed both these stories, they occurred in the form of episodes interwoven with each other and interspersed with digressions in such a way that one series of episodes — *The Poisoned Apple* — was split into four fragments and the other into eight. Malory straightens out the pattern and tells each story from beginning to end without a single interruption, occasionally adding short connecting passages so as to avoid a break between sections which in his original stood apart. The result is a narrative well suited to modern taste — a short story about Guinevere's rescue by Lancelot and another about the tragic love of the Maid of Astolat, both composed with a transparent simplicity closely approximating that of a modern work of fiction.

Needless to say, such results are rare; it is one thing to have a preference for a certain type of writing, and quite another to be conscious of the aesthetic issue involved and apply the method consistently. Hence the 'perplexities' of E. K. Chambers and others who, failing to realise that throughout Malory's work two conflicting conceptions of structure are pulling violently against each other, imagine that he has 'bungled his structural problem.' Had this been so his work would not have lived. It was his solution of the problem, partial though it was, that secured the survival of his writings. How significant this solution was, one further example will suffice to show. The story of *Balin or the Knight with the Two Swords* was originally conceived like many others as a prelude to the quest of the Grail. Challenged by King Pellam, Balin engages in a long and arduous combat in the course of which his sword is broken. Rushing into a room in the castle to find another weapon, he comes upon a sacred lance kept in the Grail sanctuary, and with it strikes the 'Dolorous Stroke' which lays waste two kingdoms. His punishment for this comes later when he unwittingly slays his brother Balan. The story thus leads from Balin's violation of the sanctuary and the Dolorous Stroke to the themes of the Blighted Land and the Maimed King as presented in the *Queste del Saint Graal* — a branch of the Cycle written long before the Balin episode. In Malory the sequence is broken. The Dolorous Stroke is not an anticipation of the Grail mysteries, but a sequel to the adventure with which the story of Balin begins: in a moment of anger Balin kills the messenger who is sent by the Lady of the Lake to ask for his head, and henceforth a curse is laid upon him and all his deeds. The dénouement is reached in the encounter with a knight whose horse is 'trapped all red, and himself in the same colour,' and in whom Balin fails to recognize his brother. And so the work as a whole is not a prelude to another work, but a tale complete in itself and marked at each end by a sharp break. Once divorced from its context it assumes both a new shape and a new meaning, as if the form were productive of substance. As we read the simple account of Balin's last battle, we do not look for any sequel that might resolve the tragic issue: the very principle of 'singleness' removes from our minds any thought of resolution or escape. Relieved of any reference to a wider scheme of things and centred upon a single human destiny, the story acquires a sense of the irretrievable, of the end 'beyond which there is nothing,' and so becomes endowed with the one unmistakable characteristic of a modern tragedy.

*
* *

The arrangement of Malory's tales in the following pages will, it is hoped, be found to be in the main consistent with his own technique as a story-teller. Except for the story of Merlin or the 'coming of Arthur' — too famous to be omitted from any representative selection — and *The Holy Grail*, these tales were conceived as independent compositions, and it seems proper, therefore, to present them as such. The addition of Malory's most mature work — *The Tale of the Death of King Arthur* — might perhaps have given a more complete idea of his manner and style, but would have upset the balance of the series and altered its character. What we have here is not the whole of Malory, but the best of Malory as he was before he wrote his one great novel: the short-story writer who is already master of his medium, but who prefers to work on a relatively small scale; a writer, moreover, who, fascinated as he is by the mere progress of adventure and dialogue, does not seek to raise the great issue of conflicting loyalties upon which the fortunes of Arthur's kingdom will break in his last romance. Each page breathes the spirit of knight-errantry as Malory understood it, of the happy and heroic life 'in Arthur's days' as he saw it, 'hung about,' as one critic said, 'with outdoor sights and sounds.' Knights 'ride into a little leafy wood' to watch a tournament, 'hold them still,' and then enter the lists and fight with such dint of strokes that the noise rings 'by the water and the wood.' Vistas of the English countryside are superimposed upon the conventional setting of the French romance, the brevities of racy speech upon the rhetorical refinements of French dialogue, and simple human relationships upon the subtleties of courtly love.

Pelleas and Ettard and *The Knight of the Cart* are examples of this last peculiarity of Malory's treatment of his material. The French originals of these tales contained in a modified but recognizable form an expression of the medieval doctrine of *courtoisie*. The story of Pelleas was the story of love requited after many disappointments. Gawain betrays the friend on whose behalf he has set out to win a lady's love; he wins it for himself, but when Pelleas discovers the betrayal he refrains from vengeance and, leaving a naked sword by the lovers' bed as a token of forgiveness, goes home resolved to die. He asks that his heart be sent after his death to his lady on a silver plate which he once received from her as a reward for his feats of bravery at a tournament. The lovers find the sword and realise that the man whom they have so cruelly betrayed has forgiven them. Conscience-stricken, they decide to make restitution to Pelleas; Gawain begs him to accept the lady's love, and Pelleas returns to the lady and marries her. From the French prose writers' point of view, Pelleas's conduct is an example of how a courtly lover should behave. Scorned by his lady, he allows himself to be ill-treated merely to obey her. In the opening episode of the story she sends out ten knights to attack him and orders him by the faith he owes her to stand still and refrain from any resistance. He obeys, and the knights bring him back to her having first tied him to his horse's tail. When she asks him whether he still has it in his heart to love her, he replies that he loves her more than ever because he knows that the suffering she has inflicted upon him will not have been borne in vain. And when finally he finds himself betrayed both by her and by Gawain he puts aside all thoughts of vengeance and is ready to die, wishing his lady more happiness than he has ever been allowed to have.

Malory's reaction to the doctrine underlying this story was that of a man bred up in arms who valued the dignity of knighthood above all else. Most of his knights are men of brief speech and unsophisticated behaviour. They engage in extraordinary adventures, but their motives admit of no sentimental refinement: they are first and foremost men of action. And so when Malory's Pelleas lets himself be tied to his horse's tail the reason is not, as in the French, that he wishes to obey his lady's capricious command, but that he hopes to gain access to her castle.

The sword which he leaves with the sleeping lovers 'overthwart both their throats' is a token not of forgiveness, but of vengeance; and naturally enough, the lady does not escape punishment: Ninive, the Lady of the Lake, casts a spell on Pelleas so as to make him hate the woman he once loved, a similar spell causing her to fall in love with Pelleas. 'So this lady Ettard died of sorrow, and the Damsel of the Lake rejoiced Sir Pelleas and loved together during their life.' In a world where vice is punished and injured men redress with their own hands the wrongs done to their honour, no other ending is possible.

On one occasion, however, in the opening passage of *The Knight of the Cart*, Malory attempts an exposition of what he thinks true love should be. He begins by saying that 'in many persons there is no stability': 'like as trees and herbs burgeoneth and flourisheth in May, in like wise every lusty heart that is in manner of lover springeth, burgeoneth, buddeth and flourisheth in lusty deeds.' Human feelings are apt to change like the seasons of the year: 'for a little blast of winter rasure anon we shall deface and lay apart true love.' A wise man should let his heart flourish in this world, 'first unto God and next unto the joy of them one has promised one's faith unto. . . . This I call virtuous love.' Love as it is to-day can be 'likened to summer and winter: soon hot, soon cold'; real love, 'the old love,' was the love that could endure, 'for men and women could love together seven years, and no lecherous lusts betwixt them, and then was love truth and faithfulness.' Virtue, he seems to suggest, lies in moderation, in the subordination of love to a higher purpose, not in a blind submission to its commands.

What, then, is to become of Lancelot, the hero of the story to which this disquisition serves as a preface? When he first appeared in Arthurian romance — in Chrétien de Troyes' *Conte de la Charrete* written between 1171 and 1173 — the cart which gave this work its title was the symbol of ignominy to which he was prepared to stoop for the sake of his lady: for, having lost his horse, he had allowed himself to be driven in a cart like one condemned, rather than fail in the rescue of Guinevere. To the Lancelot of Chrétien de Troyes any humiliation he was called upon to bear for his love was welcome; and there was no end to his humiliation: as a punishment for having hesitated for 'two steps' before getting into the cart he found himself rebuked by his lady in spite of all the trials he had faced for her sake. The story never reached Malory in this form, and the book to which he refers as *Le Chevalier de Chariot* was a prose work of the thirteenth century in which Guinevere's behaviour had been made somewhat less unnatural. She still rebuked Lancelot, but for a different reason: not because she thought that by weighing for one moment his knightly honour against his duties as a lover he had transgressed the code of courtly love, but because she knew that he had parted with her ring to Morgan le Fay. The ignominious cart was, however, still there, driven by a mysterious dwarf who promised to take Lancelot to a place where he would see the queen, and Lancelot's behaviour was still prompted by the same motives as in Chrétien de Troyes. It is only in Malory that a radical change occurs. The dwarf's cart becomes a woodman's cart driven by two men who go to fetch wood for their master, Mellyagaunce, and who offer Lancelot no help. It is he who takes the initiative, stops the cart, savagely attacks and kills one of the men and forces the other to take him to Mellyagaunce's castle, not from a sense of duty towards Guinevere, but because his armour is too heavy and uncomfortable to walk in. And just as the cart loses all symbolic value, the distant and jealously guarded land where Guinevere is held captive, the *terre foraine* from which no traveller returns, becomes part of a familiar landscape — a castle situated within a few miles of Lambeth. Lancelot reaches it in less than two hours. The journey is uneventful and he is spared many trials, among them the sword bridge which, according to all French versions, he crossed on his knees, oblivious of the pain he was inflicting upon himself and ever ready to bear any sacrifice or hardship in the service of love. 'Love in King Arthur's days,' as Malory imagined it, chivalry as he understood it, required no such trials: it implied a reasonable rule of life, a sense of loyalty without sophistication and a hierarchy of values which deprived the courtly lady of her supremacy and the theme of courtly love of its unique position in romance.

The treatment of sentiment inevitably affects the whole character of romantic imagination, and it is no accident that in medieval romance courtly idealism is associated with poetic fantasy: its natural setting is a world ruled by supernatural forces. Nothing is more characteristic of Malory's attitude to the French tradition than his frequent refusal to explain unusual occurrences in purely supernatural terms. His caution and moderation are as noticeable here as in his thoughts about 'true love.' In one of his French books there was the story of the Lady of the Lake walking to the centre of a lake upon an invisible bridge and returning with a sword for King Arthur. This Malory could not accept; and so in his account the Lady of the Lake simply tells Arthur and Merlin to take a boat and row across the lake until they come to the sword 'that the hand held.' The presence of the hand coming out of the water and holding the sword shows, if not a belief, at least some degree of acquiescence in the supernatural, which goes hand in hand with the desire to restrict the operation of supernatural forces. The invisible bridge vanishes, but the hand remains. And so it often is when Malory has to deal with magic: the marvels are not abolished, but reduced in number, and there is more realistic detail. Yet in the end the feeling of the marvellous is not lessened, but intensified. This is especially true of the story of Balin. At every stage of Balin's journey towards the enchanted castle the sense of approaching doom is enhanced by the compression of the narrative. Balin sees a cross with the inscription: 'It is not for no knight alone to ride toward this castle.' He meets an old grey-bearded man coming towards him who says, 'Thou passest thy bounds to come this way, therefore turn, and it will avail thee.' The man vanishes and Balin hears 'a horn blow as it had been the death of a beast.' 'That blast,' he says, 'is blown for me, for I am the prize, and yet I am not dead.' It matters little if after this Malory suppresses the mysterious details of Balin's reception at the castle where over a hundred maidens greet him with alluring voices to announce new enchantments. The essential magic of the tale is retained and its poetic meaning brought home to us the more clearly because it is relieved of some of its fairy-tale trappings. Malory may have 'thinned the romantic forest' and transferred what was left of it from the regions of fancy to the banks of the Thames; he has not in fact lessened its appeal. For his is a method of creative adaptation which takes traditional matter for granted and by the mere process of re-shaping and re-modelling draws new values from the old.

*

*   *

'Mysterious power of taste, of sound language, of good style,'
wrote Joseph Bédier in a preface to Jacques Boulenger's adaptation of Arthurian romances. 'Malory was but a translator, an
adaptor: and yet without him, in the England of to-day, neither
poetry, nor thought, nor art would have been exactly what
they are.' The miracle can safely be left unexpounded except
for one detail. Andrew Lang thought that Malory's style was
'based on the fresh and simple manner' of his French sources.
This is far from being the case. The manner of Malory's
French sources was neither fresh nor simple; it was laborious
and sophisticated. Like the literary English of Malory's time,
it was intended to please the intelligence, not to stir the imagination. Its texture was not unlike that of a thirteenth-century
cycle of romances: clauses were interwoven with one another
and interspersed with digressions referring to earlier or subsequent statements. But strangely enough, there is the same
contrast between this pattern and Malory's way of writing as
between his method of telling a story and the older medieval
method. One can observe in his prose the emergence of a
rhythm which raises his language to a new level of expressive-
ness. For the complex symmetry of a carefully planned period
Malory substitutes as a rule a succession of abruptly divided
clauses, some of them strikingly brief and compact, and all
modelled on the natural cadence of living speech:

> 'Certes,' said Sir Lancelot, 'all that ye have said is true, and
> from henceforward I cast me, by the grace of God, never to be so
> wicked as I have been but as to sue knighthood and do feats of
> arms.'

Each pause is clearly marked, not for its rhetorical value, but
to give a rest to the voice in a speech charged with feeling. The
corresponding French sentence is scarcely different in meaning; but instead of 'all that ye have said is true' it has a recapitu-
lation, introduced by the words 'because you have told me'
(*por ce que m'avez dit*), of what the hermit had said to Lancelot, and there is naturally no break such as 'and from hence-

forward.' A no less striking effect is achieved in the following words spoken by Galahad:

> 'Lord, I thank Thee, for now I see that that hath been my desire many a day. Now, my Blessed Lord, I would not live in this wretched world no longer if it might please Thee, Lord.'

Every one of these words is gleaned from a much longer passage. By a careful process of selection the essential threads of the original texture are unravelled so as to bring out the deeper sense of the speech, accelerate its rhythm and restore the natural emphasis of the spoken word. The 'gentle yet hardy' prose of Malory, so different from its amorphous prototype, is often the result of some such re-phrasing. Not that the spacious pages of Malory's books are always free from the dead wood of traditional rhetorical syntax or the monotony of set descriptive phrases; but once his voice is heard in its own unmistakable register it bears the narrative on with a natural rise and fall through all the vicissitudes of 'life in Arthur's days,' through the sudden changes of scenery and the complexities of romantic sentiment, as if the grace and glory of that half-forgotten world had never been and never could be lost.

*

* *

I have taken few liberties with the text. A passage has been omitted from *Balin or the Knight with the Two Swords* and another from *Lancelot and Elaine;* both passages represent digressions highly characteristic of the French romances, but not of Malory's own work. The omission, indicated in each case by suspension marks, avoids a break in the narrative in a way which Malory himself would no doubt have thought appropriate. The most important innovation is the modernisation of the spelling. Of the innumerable previous editions of Malory's works in modern orthography not a single one preserves the text as written by him; in all without exception obsolete words are removed or replaced by their modern equivalents in spite of the claim of some editors to have taken 'the most anxious care' to produce a text modernised 'as to its spelling only.'

True, the distinction between modernising the spelling and bringing the vocabulary up to date is not always easy to make, and it may legitimately be held, for instance, that to transcribe the pronoun *hir* as *their* is to substitute one form of the possessive plural for another. But as long as the form adopted exists in Malory side by side with the other and is in fact predominant, there is no great harm in preferring it and thus earning the gratitude of the lay reader. For any detailed study of Malory's language the specialist will naturally go to editions in the original spelling; all one can hope to achieve in an edition such as this is the preservation of all those pecularities of the original which are consistent with a normalised modern transcription. This applies equally to proper names. All variations in their treatment have been eliminated.

The text, apart from the spelling and a few revised readings, is the same as that of my three-volume edition of *The Works of Sir Thomas Malory* (Oxford, 1947). It is based upon a collation of the manuscript discovered in 1934 in the Fellows' Library of Winchester College with Caxton's *Le Morte Darthur* and with Malory's sources. The manuscript having lost a gathering of eight leaves at each end and a few leaves in the middle, Caxton is our only authority for certain sections of the text including the first of the tales published here and part of the second.

The footnotes are intended to facilitate the reading of the text by means of such renderings and comments as would otherwise have required the addition of a glossary. A certain degree of familiarity with obsolete words and constructions is, of course, assumed, and some simple words and phrases such as *brent* (burnt), *brast* (burst), *dole* (sorrow), *essay* (try), *on life* (alive), *or* (before), *swough* (swoon), *syn, sith*[*en*] (since), *that* in the sense of 'so that' etc., left unexplained; but an attempt is made to give the meaning of unusual or polyvalent words and to elucidate the less intelligible passages. The only abbreviations used are *M* for Malory, *O* for the 1947 edition of his works, and *F* for the French texts which represent his sources. To conform to the general pattern of the series I have dispensed with the Index of proper names. Anyone unduly puzzled by these and tempted to turn to the end of the volume should recall the warning contained in the preface to a famous translation of Plutarch: 'As for the strange names, stick not in them, for who that can take no fruit in it without he know clearly every tale that is here touched, I would he should not read this book.'

KING ARTHUR
AND HIS KNIGHTS

Merlin

It befell in the days of Uther Pendragon, when he was king
of all England and so reigned, that there was a mighty duke
in Cornwall that held war against him long time, and the duke
was called the duke of Tintagel. And so by means King
Uther sent for this duke, charging him to bring his wife with
him, for she was called a fair lady and a passing wise, and her
name was called Igraine.

So when the duke and his wife were come unto the king, by
the means of great lords they were accorded [1] both. The king
liked and loved this lady well, and he made them great cheer
out of measure, and desired to have lain by her. But she was
a passing good woman, and would not assent unto the king.
And then she told the duke her husband, and said,

'I suppose that we were sent for that I should be dishonoured. Wherefore, husband, I counsel you that we depart
from hence suddenly, that we may ride all night unto our
own castle.'

And in like wise as she said so they departed, that neither
the king nor none of his council were ware of their departing. Also [2] soon as King Uther knew of their departing so
suddenly, he was wonderly wroth; then he called to him his
privy council and told them of the sudden departing of the
duke and his wife. Then they advised the king to send for the
duke and his wife by a great charge:

'And if he will not come at your summons, then may ye
do your best; then have ye cause to make mighty war upon
him.'

So that was done, and the messengers had their answers;

1 reconciled   2 as

3

and that was this, shortly, that neither he nor his wife would not come at [3] him. Then was the king wonderly wroth; and then the king sent him plain word again and bade him be ready and stuff him and garnish him,[4] for within forty days he would fetch him out of the biggest castle that he hath.

When the duke had this warning, anon he went and furnished and garnished two strong castles of his, of the which the one hight Tintagel, and the other castle hight Terrabil. So his wife Dame Igraine he put in the castle of Tintagel, and himself he put in the castle of Terrabil, the which had many issues and posterns out. Then in all haste came Uther with a great host and laid a siege about the castle of Terrabil, and there he pight [5] many pavilions. And there was great war made on both parties and much people slain.

Then for pure anger and for great love of fair Igraine the king Uther fell sick. So came to the king Uther Sir Ulfius, a noble knight, and asked the king why he was sick.

'I shall tell thee,' said the king, 'I am sick for anger and for love of fair Igraine, that I may not be whole.'

'Well, my lord,' said Sir Ulfius, 'I shall seek Merlin and he shall do you remedy, that your heart shall be pleased.'

So Ulfius departed and by adventure he met Merlin in a beggar's array, and there Merlin asked Ulfius whom he sought, and he said he had little ado [6] to tell him.

'Well,' said Merlin, 'I know whom thou seekest, for thou seekest Merlin; therefore seek no farther, for I am he. And if King Uther will well reward me and be sworn unto me to fulfil my desire, that shall be his honour and profit more than mine, for I shall cause him to have all his desire.'

'All this will I undertake,' said Ulfius, 'that there shall be nothing reasonable but thou shalt have thy desire.'

'Well,' said Merlin, 'he shall have his intent and desire. And therefore,' said Merlin, 'ride on your way, for I will not be long behind.'

Then Ulfius was glad and rode on more than a pace [7] till that he came to King Uther Pendragon and told him he had met with Merlin.

---

[3] wished to come to
[4] furnish himself with men and stores
[5] set up
[6] reason
[7] at a good speed

'Where is he?' said the king.

'Sir,' said Ulfius, 'he will not dwell [8] long.'

Therewithal Ulfius was ware where Merlin stood at the porch of the pavilion's door, and then Merlin was bound to come to the king. When King Uther saw him he said he was welcome.

'Sir,' said Merlin, 'I know all your heart every deal.[9] So [10] ye will be sworn unto me, as ye be a true king anointed, to fulfil my desire, ye shall have your desire.'

Then the king was sworn upon the four Evangelists.

'Sir,' said Merlin, 'this is my desire: the first night that ye shall lie by Igraine ye shall get a child on her; and when that is born, that it shall be delivered to me for to nourish thereas [11] I will have it; for it shall be your worship and the child's avail [12] as mickle as the child is worth.

'I will well,' said the king, 'as thou wilt have it.'

'Now make you ready,' said Merlin. 'This night ye shall lie with Igraine in the castle of Tintagel. And ye shall be like the duke her husband, Ulfius shall be like Sir Brastias, a knight of the duke's, and I will be like a knight that hight Sir Jordanus, a knight of the duke's. But wait [13] ye make not many questions with her nor her men, but say ye are diseased,[14] and so hie you to bed and rise not on the morn till I come to you, for the castle of Tintagel is but ten mile hence.'

So this was done as they devised. But the duke of Tintagel espied how the king rode from the siege of Terrabil. And therefore that night he issued out of the castle at a postern for to have distressed [15] the king's host, and so through his own issue [16] the duke himself was slain or ever the king came at the castle of Tintagel. So after the death of the duke King Uther lay with Igraine, more than three hours after his death, and begat on her that night Arthur; and or day came Merlin came to the king and bade him make him ready, and so he kissed the lady Igraine and departed in all haste. But when the lady heard tell of the duke her husband, and by all record

[8] tarry
[9] all that is in your heart
[10] provided that
[11] where
[12] advantage
[13] take care
[14] indisposed
[15] in order to attack
[16] sortie

he was dead or ever King Uther came to her, then she marvelled who that might be that lay with her in likeness of her lord. So she mourned privily and held her peace.

Then all the barons by one assent prayed the king of accord betwixt the lady Igraine and him. The king gave them leave,[17] for fain would he have been accorded with her; so the king put all the trust in Ulfius to entreat [18] between them. So by the entreaty at the last the king and she met together.

'Now will we do well,' [19] said Ulfius. 'Our king is a lusty knight and wifeless, and my lady Igraine is a passing fair lady; it were great joy unto us all an it might please the king to make her his queen.'

Unto that they all well accorded and moved it to the king. And anon, like a lusty knight, he assented thereto with good will, and so in all haste they were married in a morning with great mirth and joy.

And King Lot of Lothian and of Orkney then wedded Margawse that was Gawain's mother, and King Nentres of the land of Garlot wedded Elaine. All this was done at the request of King Uther. And the third sister, Morgan le Fay, was put to school in a nunnery, and there she learned so much that she was a great clerk of necromancy. And after she was wedded to King Uriens of the land of Gore, that was Sir Uwain's le Blanchemain's father.

Then Queen Igraine waxed daily greater and greater. So it befell after within half a year, as King Uther lay by his queen, he asked her, by the faith she owed to him, whose was the child within her body. Then was she sore abashed to give answer.[20]

'Dismay you not,' said the king, 'but tell me the truth, and I shall love you the better, by the faith of my body!' [1]

'Sir,' said she, 'I shall tell you the truth. The same night that my lord was dead, the hour of his death, as his knights record, there came into my castle of Tintagel a man like my lord in speech and in countenance, and two knights with him in likeness of his two knights Brastias and Jordanus, and so I went unto bed with him as I ought to do with my lord; and

---

[17] granted their request
[18] negotiate
[19] do the right thing

[20] silent from confusion
[1] my faith

the same night, as I shall answer unto God, this child was begotten upon me.'

'That is truth,' said the king, 'as ye say, for it was I myself that came in the likeness. And therefore dismay you not, for I am father of the child'; and there he told her all the cause [2] how it was by Merlin's counsel. Then the queen made great joy when she knew who was the father of her child.

Soon came Merlin unto the king and said,

'Sir, ye must purvey you [3] for the nourishing of your child.'

'As thou wilt,' said the king, 'be it.'

'Well,' said Merlin, 'I know a lord of yours in this land that is a passing true man and a faithful, and he shall have the nourishing of your child; and his name is Sir Ector, and he is a lord of fair livelihood [4] in many parts in England and Wales. And this lord, Sir Ector, let him be sent for for to come and speak with you, and desire him yourself, as he loveth you, that he will put his own child to nourishing to another woman and that his wife nourish yours. And when the child is born let it be delivered to me at yonder privy postern unchristened.'

So like as Merlin devised it was done. And when Sir Ector was come he made fiaunce [5] to the king for to nourish the child like as the king desired; and there the king granted Sir Ector great rewards. Then when the lady was delivered the king commanded two knights and two ladies to take the child bound in a cloth of gold, 'and that ye deliver him to what poor man ye meet at the postern gate of the castle.' So the child was delivered unto Merlin, and so he bare it forth unto Sir Ector, and made an holy man to christen him, and named him Arthur. And so Sir Ector's wife nourished him with her own pap.

Then within two years King Uther fell sick of a great malady. And in the meanwhile his enemies usurped upon him [6] and did a great battle upon his men and slew many of his people.

'Sir,' said Merlin, 'ye may not lie so as ye do, for ye must to the field, though ye ride on an horse-litter. For ye shall never

[2] the whole matter
[3] arrange
[4] possessions
[5] promised
[6] encroached upon his land

have the better of your enemies but if your person be there, and then shall ye have the victory.'

So it was done as Merlin had devised, and they carried the king forth in an horse-litter with a great host towards his enemies, and at St. Albans there met with the king a great host of the North.[7] And that day Sir Ulfius and Sir Brastias did great deeds of arms, and King Uther's men overcame the Northern battle [8] and slew many people and put the remnant to flight; and then the king returned unto London and made great joy of his victory.

And then he fell passing sore sick, so that three days and three nights he was speechless; wherefore all the barons made great sorrow and asked Merlin what counsel were best.

'There is none other remedy,' said Merlin, 'but God will have His will. But look ye all barons be before King Uther to-morn, and God and I shall make him to speak.'

So on the morn all the barons with Merlin came tofore the king. Then Merlin said aloud unto King Uther.

'Sir, shall your son Arthur be king after your days of this realm with all the appurtenance?' [9]

Then Uther Pendragon turned him and said in hearing of them all,

'I give him God's blessing and mine, and bid him pray for my soul, and righteously and worshipfully that he claim the crown upon forfeiture of my blessing;' and therewith he yielded up the ghost. And then was he interred as longed [10] to a king, wherefore the queen, fair Igraine, made great sorrow, and all the barons.

Then stood the realm in great jeopardy long while, for every lord that was mighty of men made him strong, and many weened to have been [11] king. Then Merlin went to the Archbishop of Canterbury and counselled him for to send for all the lords of the realm and all the gentlemen of arms, that they should to London come by Christmas upon pain of cursing, and for this cause, that Jesu, that was born on that

---

[7] *Probably a reminiscence of the first battle of St. Albans (22 May 1455) when another sick king, Henry VI, was carried forth at the head of his troops to meet a rebel army.*

[8] army

[9] privileges belonging to the crown

[10] befitted

[11] expected to be made

night, that He would of His great mercy show some miracle, as He was come to be King of mankind, for to show some miracle who should be rightwise king of this realm. So the Archbishop, by the advice of Merlin, sent for all the lords and gentlemen of arms that they should come by Christmas even unto London; and many of them made them clean of their life, that their prayer might be the more acceptable unto God.

So in the greatest church of London, whether it were Paul's or not the French book maketh no mention, all the estates were long or day [12] in the church for to pray. And when matins and the first mass was done there was seen in the churchyard, against the high altar, a great stone four square, like unto a marble stone, and in midst thereof was like an anvil of steel a foot on high, and therein stuck a fair sword naked by the point, and letters there were written in gold about the sword that said thus: 'WHOSO PULLETH OUT THIS SWORD OF THIS STONE AND ANVIL IS RIGHTWISE KING BORN OF ALL ENGLAND.' Then the people marvelled and told it to the Archbishop.

'I command,' said the Archbishop, 'that ye keep you within your church and pray unto God still; that no man touch the sword till the high mass be all done.'

So when all masses were done all the lords went to behold the stone and the sword. And when they saw the scripture some essayed, such as would have been king, but none might stir the sword nor move it.

'He is not here,' said the Archbishop, 'that shall achieve the sword, but doubt not God will make him known. But this is my counsel,' said the Archbishop, 'that we let purvey ten knights, men of good fame, and they to keep this sword.'

So it was ordained, and then there was made a cry that every man should essay that would for to win the sword. And upon New Year's Day the barons let make a jousts and a tournament, that all knights that would joust or tourney there might play. And all this was ordained for to keep the lords together and the commons, for the Archbishop trusted that God would make him known that should win the sword.

So upon New Year's Day, when the service was done, the

[12] long before dawn

barons rode unto the field, some to joust and some to tourney. And so it happed that Sir Ector, that had great livelihood [13] about London, rode unto the jousts, and with him rode Sir Kay, his son, and young Arthur that was his nourished brother; and Sir Kay was made knight at All Hallowmass afore. So as they rode to the jousts-ward Sir Kay had lost [14] his sword, for he had left it at his father's lodging, and so he prayed young Arthur for to ride for his sword.

'I will well,' said Arthur, and rode fast after the sword.

And when he came home the lady and all were out to see the jousting. Then was Arthur wroth, and said to himself, 'I will ride to the churchyard and take the sword with me that sticketh in the stone, for my brother Sir Kay shall not be without a sword this day.' So when he came to the churchyard Sir Arthur alight and tied his horse to the stile, and so he went to the tent and found no knights there, for they were at the jousting. And so he handled the sword by the handles, and lightly and fiercely [15] pulled it out of the stone, and took his horse and rode his way until he came to his brother Sir Kay and delivered him the sword.

And as soon as Sir Kay saw the sword he wist well it was the sword of the stone, and so he rode to his father Sir Ector and said,

'Sir, lo here is the sword of the stone, wherefore I must be king of this land.'

When Sir Ector beheld the sword he returned again [16] and came to the church, and there they alight all three and went into the church, and anon he made Sir Kay to swear upon a book how he came to that sword.

'Sir,' said Sir Kay, 'by my brother Arthur, for he brought it to me.'

'How gat ye this sword?' said Sir Ector to Arthur.

'Sir, I will tell you. When I came home for my brother's sword I found nobody at home to deliver me his sword, and so I thought my brother Sir Kay should not be swordless, and so I came hither eagerly [17] and pulled it out of the stone without any pain.' [18]

'Found ye any knights about this sword?' said Sir Ector.

---

13 estates
14 missed
15 quickly and vigorously

16 went back
17 quickly
18 difficulty

'Nay,' said Arthur.

'Now,' said Sir Ector to Arthur, 'I understand ye must be king of this land.'

'Wherefore I?' said Arthur, 'and for what cause?'

'Sir,' said Ector, 'for God will have it so, for there should never man have drawn out this sword but he that shall be rightwise king of this land. Now let me see whether ye can put the sword thereas [19] it was and pull it out again.'

'That is no mastery,' [20] said Arthur, and so he put it in the stone. Therewithal Sir Ector essayed to pull out the sword and failed.

'Now essay,' said Sir Ector unto Sir Kay. And anon he pulled at the sword with all his might, but it would not be.

'Now shall ye essay,' said Sir Ector to Arthur.

'I will well,' said Arthur, and pulled it out easily.

And therewithal Sir Ector kneeled down to the earth and Sir Kay.

'Alas!' said Arthur, 'my own dear father and brother, why kneel ye to me?'

'Nay, nay, my lord Arthur, it is not so. I was never your father nor of your blood, but I wot well ye are of an higher blood than I weened ye were,' and then Sir Ector told him all, how he was betaken [1] him for to nourish him and by whose commandment, and by Merlin's deliverance.[2]

Then Arthur made great dole when he understood that Sir Ector was not his father.

'Sir,' said Ector unto Arthur, 'will ye be my good and gracious lord when ye are king?'

'Else were I to blame,' said Arthur, 'for ye are the man in the world that I am most beholding to, and my good lady and mother your wife that as well as her own hath fostered me and kept. And if ever it be God's will that I be king as ye say, ye shall desire of me what I may do, and I shall not fail you. God forbid I should fail you.'

'Sir,' said Sir Ector, 'I will ask no more of you but that ye will make my son, your foster brother Sir Kay, seneschal of all your lands.'

[19] where
[20] deed of prowess
[1] entrusted to

[2] and how he was handed over to Sir Ector by Merlin

'That shall be done,' said Arthur, 'and more, by the faith of my body, that never man shall have that office but he while he and I live.'

Therewithal they went unto the Archbishop and told him how the sword was achieved and by whom. And on Twelfth-day all the barons came thither and to essay to take the sword who that would essay, but there afore them all there might none take it out but Arthur. Wherefore there were many lords wroth, and said it was great shame unto them all and the realm to be overgoverned with a boy of no high blood born. And so they fell out at that time, that [3] it was put off till Candlemas, and then all the barons should meet there again; but always the ten knights were ordained to watch the sword day and night, and so they set a pavilion over the stone and the sword, and five always watched.

So at Candlemas many more great lords came thither for to have won the sword, but there might none prevail. And right as Arthur did at Christmas he did at Candlemas, and pulled out the sword easily, whereof the barons were sore aggrieved and put it off in delay till the high feast of Easter. And as Arthur sped afore so did he at Easter. Yet there were some of the great lords had indignation that Arthur should be king, and put it off in a delay till the feast of Pentecost. Then the Archbishop of Canterbury, by Merlin's providence,[4] let purvey [5] then of the best knights that they might get, and such knights as Uther Pendragon loved best and most trusted in his days, and such knights were put about Arthur as Sir Baudwin of Britain, Sir Kaynes, Sir Ulfius, Sir Brastias; all these with many other were always about Arthur day and night till the feast of Pentecost.

And at the feast of Pentecost all manner of men essayed to pull at the sword that would essay, but none might prevail but Arthur, and he pulled it out afore all the lords and commons that were there. Wherefore all the commons cried at once,

'We will have Arthur unto our king! We will put him no more in delay, for we all see that it is God's will that he shall be our king, and who that holdeth against it we will slay him!'

---

[3] with the result that   [5] appoint
[4] contriving

And therewithal they kneeled at once, both rich and poor, and cried Arthur mercy because they had delayed him so long. And Arthur forgave them, and took the sword between both his hands and offered it upon the altar where the Archbishop was, and so was he made knight of the best man that was there.

And so anon was the coronation made, and there was he sworn unto his lords and the commons for to be a true king, to stand with true justice from thenceforth the days of this life. Also then he made all lords that held of the crown to come in and to do service as they ought to do. And many complaints were made unto Sir Arthur of great wrongs that were done since the death of King Uther, of many lands that were bereaved lords, knights, ladies, and gentlemen; wherefore King Arthur made the lands to be given again unto them that ought them.[6]

When this was done, that the king had stablished [7] all the countries about London, then he let make Sir Kay seneschal of England; and Sir Baudwin of Britain was made constable, and Sir Ulfius was made chamberlain, and Sir Brastias was made warden to wait upon the North from Trent forwards, for it was that time the most party the king's enemies. But within few years after Arthur won all the North, Scotland and all that were under their obeissance, also Wales. A part of it held against Arthur, but he overcame them all as he did the remnant,[8] through the noble prowess of himself and his knights of the Round Table.[9]

---

[6] to whom they rightfully belonged

[7] restored order to

[8] the rest

[9] *According to the French romance, the Round Table was at that time the property of King* *Leodegan, who had received it as a present from King Uther. When Arthur married Guinevere, King Leodegan's daughter, she brought the Round Table with her as part of her dowry.*

Balin

or The Knight with the Two Swords

After the death of Uther reigned Arthur, his son, which had great war in his days for to get all England into his hand; for there were many kings within the realm of England and of Scotland, Wales and Cornwall.

So it befell on a time when King Arthur was at London, there came a knight and told the king tidings how the King Rions of North Wales had reared [1] a great number of people, and were entered in the land and brent and slew the king's true liege people.

'If this be true,' said Arthur, 'it were great shame unto mine estate [2] but that he were mightily withstood.'

'It is truth,' said the knight, 'for I saw the host myself.'

'Well,' said the king, 'I shall ordain to withstand his malice.' [3]

Then the king let make a cry that all the lords, knights and gentlemen of arms should draw unto the castle called Camelot in those days, and there the king would let make a council-general and a great jousts. So when the king was come thither with all his baronage and lodged as they seemed best, also there was come a damsel the which was sent from the great Lady Lyle of Avalon.[4] And when she came before King Arthur she told from whence she came, and how she was sent on message unto him for these causes. Then she let her

---

[1] raised
[2] insult to my dignity
[3] evil design
[4] F: *Dame de l'Isle Avalon*

15

mantle fall that was richly furred, and then was she girt with
a noble sword, whereof the king had marvel and said,

'Damsel, for what cause are ye girt with that sword? It
beseemeth you nought.' [5]

'Now shall I tell you,' said the damsel. 'This sword that I
am girt withal doth me great sorrow and cumbrance, for I
may not be delivered of this sword but by a knight, and he
must be a passing good man of his hands and of his deeds, and
without villainy other treachery,[6] and without treason. And
if I may find such a knight that hath all these virtues, he may
draw out this sword out of the sheath. For I have been at
King Rions, for it was told me there were passing good
knights; and he and all his knights hath essayed and none can
speed.'

'This is a great marvel,' said Arthur. 'If this be sooth I will
essay myself to draw out the sword, not presuming myself
that I am the best knight; but I will begin to draw your sword
in giving an example to all the barons, that they shall essay
everych one after other when I have essayed.'

Then Arthur took the sword by the sheath and girdle and
pulled at it eagerly, but the sword would not out.

'Sir,' said the damsel, 'ye need not for to pull half so sore,[7]
for he that shall pull it out shall do it with little might.'

'Ye say well,' said Arthur. 'Now essay ye all, my barons.'

'But beware ye be not defiled with shame, treachery, neither
guile, for then it will not avail,' said the damsel, 'for he must
be a clean knight without villainy and of gentle strain of
father side and of mother side.'

The most part of all the barons of the Round Table that
were there at that time essayed all by row,[8] but there might
none speed. Wherefore the damsel made great sorrow out of
measure and said,

'Alas! I weened in this court had been the best knights of
the world without treachery other treason.'

'By my faith,' said Arthur, 'here are good knights, as I deem,
as any be in the world, but their grace is not [9] to help you,
wherefore I am sore displeased.'

Then it befell so that time there was a poor knight with

---

[5] it does not become you
[6] deceit (*Old Fr.: tricherie*)
[7] hard

[8] in turn (M: *rew*)
[9] they have not had the good
fortune

King Arthur that had been prisoner with him half a year for slaying of a knight which was cousin unto King Arthur. And the name of this knight was called Balin, and by good means of the barons he was delivered out of prison, for he was a good man named of his body, and he was born in Northumberland. And so he went privily into the court and saw this adventure whereof it raised his heart, and would essayed [10] as other knights did. But for he was poor and poorly arrayed, he put himself not far in press. But in his heart he was fully assured to do as well, if his grace happed him,[11] as any knight that there was. And as the damsel took her leave of Arthur and of all the barons, so departing, this knight Balin called unto her and said,

'Damsel, I pray you of your courtesy suffer me as well to essay as these other lords. Though that I be poorly arrayed yet in my heart meseemeth I am fully assured [12] as some of these other, and meseemeth in mine heart to speed right well.'

This damsel then beheld this poor knight and saw he was a likely [13] man; but for his poor arrayment she thought he should not be of no worship [14] without villainy or treachery. And then she said unto that knight,

'Sir, it needeth not you to put me to no more pain,[15] for it seemeth [16] not you to speed thereas [17] all these other knights have failed.'

'Ah, fair damsel,' said Balin, 'worthiness and good tatches [18] and also good deeds is not only in arrayment, but manhood and worship is hid within a man's person; and many a worshipful knight is not known unto all people. And therefore worship and hardiness [19] is not in arrayment.'

'By God,' said the damsel, 'ye say sooth, therefore ye shall essay to do what ye may.'

Then Balin took the sword by the girdle and sheath and drew it out easily; and when he looked on the sword it pleased him much. Then had the king and all the barons great marvel that Balin had done that adventure; many knights had great despite [20] at him.

[10] wished to try it
[11] if fortune favoured him
[12] confident
[13] handsome
[14] could not be a person of quality
[15] any further trouble
[16] becomes
[17] where
[18] qualities
[19] nobility and valour
[20] anger

'Certes,' said the damsel, 'this is a passing good knight and the best that ever I found, and most of worship without treason, treachery, or felony. And many marvels shall he do. Now, gentle and courteous knight, give me the sword again.'

'Nay,' said Balin, 'for this sword will I keep but it be taken from me with force.'

'Well,' said the damsel, 'ye are not wise to keep the sword from me, for ye shall slay with that sword the best friend that ye have and the man that ye most love in the world, and that sword shall be your destruction.'

'I shall take the adventure,' said Balin, 'that God will ordain for me. But the sword ye shall not have at this time, by the faith of my body!'

'Ye shall repent it within short time,' said the damsel, 'for I would have the sword more for your advantage than for mine; for I am passing heavy [1] for your sake, for an ye will not leave that sword it shall be your destruction, and that is great pity.'

So with that departed the damsel and great sorrow she made. And anon after Balin sent for his horse and armour, and so would depart from the court, and took his leave of King Arthur.

'Nay,' said the king, 'I suppose ye will not [2] depart so lightly from this fellowship. I suppose that ye are displeased that I have showed you unkindness. But blame me the less, for I was misinformed against you: but I weened ye had not been such a knight as ye are of worship and prowess. And if ye will abide in this court among my fellowship, I shall so advance you as ye shall be pleased.'

'God thank your Highness,' said Balin. 'Your bounty may no man praise half unto the value, but at this time I must needs depart, beseeching you always of your good grace.'

'Truly,' said the king, 'I am right wroth of your departing. But I pray you, fair knight, that ye tarry not long from me, and ye shall be right welcome unto me and to my barons, and I shall amend all miss that [3] I have done against you.'

'God thank your good grace,' said Balin, and therewith made him ready to depart. Then the most party of the knights of the Round Table said that Balin did not this adventure all only by might but by witchcraft.

---

[1] sad
[2] I do not expect you to
[3] such wrong as

So the meanwhile that this knight was making him ready to depart there came into the court the Lady of the Lake, and she came on horseback richly beseen,[4] and salewed King Arthur and there asked him a gift that he promised her when she gave him the sword.

'That is sooth,' said Arthur, 'a gift I promised you, but I have forgotten the name of my sword[5] that ye gave me.'

'The name of it,' said the lady, 'is Excalibur, that is as much to say as Cut Steel.'

'Ye say well,' said the king. 'Ask what ye will and ye shall have it an it lie in my power to give it.'

'Well,' said this lady, 'then I ask the head of this knight that hath won this sword, other else the damsel's head that brought it. I take no force though[6] I have both their heads: for he slew my brother, a good knight and a true; and that gentlewoman was causer of my father's death.'

'Truly,' said King Arthur, 'I may not grant you neither of their heads with my worship;[7] therefore ask what ye will else, and I shall fulfil your desire.'

'I will ask none other thing,' said the lady.

So when Balin was ready to depart, he saw the Lady of the Lake which by her means had slain his mother; and he had sought her three year before. And when it was told him how she had asked his head of King Arthur, he went to her straight and said,

'Evil be ye found:[8] ye would have mine head, and therefore ye shall lose yours!'

And with his sword lightly[9] he smote off her head before King Arthur.

'Alas, for shame!' said the king. 'Why have ye do so? Ye have shamed me and all my court, for this lady was a lady that I was much beholding to, and hither she came under my safe-conduct. Therefore I shall never forgive you that trespass.'[10]

'Sir,' said Balin, 'me forthinketh of[11] your displeasure, for this same lady was the untruest lady living, and by enchant-

---

[4] dressed
[5] *A misreading of the French* 'je vos obliai a demander' ('*I forgot to ask you*')
[6] I do not care if
[7] honour forbids me to grant you either
[8] may you be cursed
[9] quickly
[10] offence
[11] I grieve at

ment and by sorcery she hath been the destroyer of many
good knights, and she was causer that my mother was brent
through her falsehood and treachery.'

'For what cause soever [12] ye had,' said Arthur, 'ye should
have forborne in my presence. Therefore think not the con-
trary; ye shall repent it, for such another despite [13] had I
never in my court. Therefore withdraw you out of my court
in all the haste that ye may!'

Then Balin took up the head of the lady and bore it with
him to his ostry,[14] and there met with his squire that was
sorry he had displeased King Arthur, and so they rode forth
out of town.

'Now,' said Balin, 'we must depart; therefore take thou
this head and bear it to my friends and tell them how I have
sped, and tell them in Northumberland how my most foe is
dead. Also tell them how I am out of prison, and what adventure befell me at the getting of this sword.'

'Alas!' said the squire, 'ye are greatly to blame for to displease King Arthur.'

'As for that,' said Balin, 'I will hie me in all the haste that
I may to meet with King Rions and destroy him, other else
to die therefore.[15] And if it may hap me [16] to win him, then
will King Arthur be my good friend.'

'Sir, where shall I meet with you?' said his squire.

'In King Arthur's court,' said Balin.

So his squire and he departed at that time. Then King
Arthur and all the court made great dole and had great shame
of the Lady of the Lake. Then the king buried her richly.

So at that time there was a knight the which was the king's
son of Ireland, and his name was Lanceor, the which was an
orgulous [17] knight and accounted himself one of the best of
the court. And he had great despite [18] at Balin for the achiev-
ing of the sword, that any should be accounted more hardy [19]
or more of prowess, and he asked King Arthur license to
ride after Balin and to revenge the despite [20] that he had done.

[12] whatever reason
[13] insult
[14] lodging
[15] or die in the attempt
[16] if I should have the good fortune

[17] proud, boastful
[18] resentment
[19] brave
[20] avenge the wrong

'Do your best,' said Arthur. 'I am right wroth with Balin. I would he were quit of the despite [1] that he hath done unto me and my court.'

Then this Lanceor went to his ostry [2] to make him ready. So in the meanwhile came Merlin unto the court of King Arthur, and anon was told him the adventure of the sword and the death of the Lady of the Lake.

'Now shall I say you,' said Merlin; 'this same damsel that here standeth,[3] that brought the sword unto your court, I shall tell you the cause of her coming. She is the falsest damsel that liveth — she shall not say nay! For she hath a brother, a passing good knight of prowess and a full true man, and this damsel loved another knight that held her as paramour. And this good knight, her brother, met with the knight that held her to paramour, and slew him by force of his hands. And when this false damsel understood this she went to the Lady Lyle of Avalon and took her his sword and besought her of help to be revenged on her own brother.

'And so this Lady Lyle of Avalon took her this sword that she brought with her, and told there should no man pull it out of the sheath but if he be one of the best knights of this realm, and he should be hardy [4] and full of prowess; and with that sword he should slay his brother. This was the cause, damsel, that ye came into this court. I know it as well as ye. God would ye had not come here; but ye came never in fellowship of worshipful folk for to do good, but always great harm. And that knight that hath achieved the sword shall be destroyed through the sword; for the which will be great damage,[5] for there liveth not a knight of more prowess than he is. And he shall do unto you, my lord Arthur, great honour and kindness; and it is great pity he shall not endure but a while, for of his strength and hardiness [6] I know him not living his match.'

So this knight of Ireland armed him at all points and dressed his shield on his shoulder and mounted upon horseback and

---

[1] I wish he would redeem the wrong
[2] lodging
[3] *The French romance says that the damsel had in the meantime returned to court*
[4] brave
[5] pity
[6] bravery

took his glaive [7] in his hand, and rode after a great pace as much as his horse might drive.[8] And within a little space, on a mountain, he had a sight of Balin, and with a loud voice he cried,

'Abide, knight! for else ye shall abide whether ye will either no! And the shield that is tofore you shall not help you,' said this Irish knight, 'therefore come I after you.'

'Peradventure,' [9] said Balin, 'ye had been better to have hold you at home. For many a man weeneth to put his enemy to a rebuke,[10] and oft it falleth on himself. Out of what court be ye come from?' said Balin.

'I am come from the court of King Arthur,' said the knight of Ireland, 'that am come hither to revenge the despite [11] ye did this day unto King Arthur and to his court.'

'Well,' said Balin, 'I see well I must have ado with you; that me forthinketh [12] that I have grieved King Arthur or any of his court. And your quarrel is full simple,' said Balin, 'unto me;[13] for the lady that is dead did to me great damage, and else I would have been loath as any knight that liveth for to slay a lady.'

'Make you ready,' said the knight Lanceor, 'and dress you unto me,[14] for that one [15] shall abide in the field.'

Then they feautred [16] their spears in their rests and came together as much as their horses might drive. And the Irish knight smote Balin on the shield that all went to shivers off his spear. And Balin smote him again through the shield, and the hauberk perished, and so bore him through the body and over the horse crupper; and anon turned his horse fiercely and drew out his sword, and wist not that he had slain him.

Then [17] he saw him lie as a dead corpse, he looked about him and was ware of a damsel that came riding full fast as the horse might drive, on a fair palfrey. And when she espied that Lanceor was slain she made sorrow out of measure and said,

'Ah! Balin, two bodies thou hast slain in one heart, and two hearts in one body, and two souls thou hast lost.'

---

[7] lance
[8] as fast as his horse could go
[9] perchance
[10] expects to defeat his opponent
[11] avenge the wrong
[12] much as it distresses me

[13] you have little reason to pick a quarrel with me
[14] prepare to fight with me
[15] one of us
[16] fixed
[17] when

And therewith she took the sword from her love that lay dead, and fell to the ground in a swoon. And when she arose she made great dole out of measure, which sorrow grieved Balin passingly sore. And he went unto her for to have taken the sword out of her hand; but she held it so fast he might not take it out of her hand but if he should have hurt her. And suddenly she set the pommel to the ground, and rove [18] herself throughout the body.

When Balin espied her deeds he was passing heavy in his heart and ashamed that so fair a damsel had destroyed herself for the love of [19] his death. 'Alas!' said Balin, 'me repenteth sore the death of this knight for the love of [19] this damsel, for there was much true love betwixt them.' And so for sorrow he might no longer behold them, but turned his horse and looked toward a fair forest.

And then was he ware by his arms that there came riding his brother Balan. And when they were met they put off their helms and kissed together and wept for joy and pity. Then Balan said,

'Brother, I little weened to have met with you at this sudden adventure, but I am right glad of your deliverance of your dolorous prisonment: for a man told me in the Castle of Four Stones that ye were delivered, and that man had seen you in the court of King Arthur. And therefore I came hither into this country, for here I supposed to find you.'

And anon Balin told his brother of his adventure of the sword and the death of the Lady of the Lake, and how King Arthur was displeased with him.

'Wherefore he sent this knight after me that lieth here dead. And the death of this damsel grieveth me sore.'

'So doth it me,' said Balan, 'but ye must take the adventure that God will ordain you.'

'Truly,' said Balan, 'I am right heavy that my lord Arthur is displeased with me, for he is the most worshipfullest king that reigneth now in earth; and his love I will get other else I will put my life in adventure.[20] For King Rions lieth at the siege of the Castle Terrabil, and thither will we draw in all goodly haste to prove our worship and prowess upon him.'

'I will well,' said Balan, 'that ye do so; and I will ride with

[18] stabbed   [20] risk my life
[19] because of

you and put my body in adventure [20] with you, as a brother ought to do.'

'Now go we hence,' said Balin, 'and well we be met.'

The meanwhile as they talked there came a dwarf from the city of Camelot on horseback as much as he might,[1] and found the dead bodies; wherefore he made great dole, and pulled his hair for sorrow, and said,

'Which of two knights have done this deed?'

'Whereby asketh thou?' said Balan.

'For I would wit,' said the dwarf.

'It was I,' said Balin, 'that slew this knight in my defendant;[2] for hither he came to chase me, and either I must slay him either he me. And this damsel slew herself for his love, which repenteth me. And for her sake I shall owe all women the better will and service all the days of my life.'

'Alas!' said the dwarf, 'thou hast done great damage unto thyself. For this knight that is here dead was one of the most valiant men that lived. And trust well, Balin, the kin of this knight will chase you through the world till they have slain you.'

'As for that,' said Balin, 'thee I fear not greatly; but I am right heavy that I should diplease my lord, King Arthur, for the death of this knight.'

So as they talked together there came a king of Cornwall riding, which hight King Mark. And when he saw these two bodies dead, and understood how they were dead by the two knights above-said, then made the king great sorrow for the true love that was betwixt them, and said, 'I will not depart till I have on this earth made a tomb.' And there he pight [3] his pavilions and sought all the country to find a tomb, and in a church they found one was fair and rich. And then the king let put them both in the earth, and laid the tomb upon them, and wrote the names of them both on the tomb, how 'here lieth Lanceor, the king's son of Ireland, that at his own request was slain by the hands of Balin,' and how 'this lady Columbe and paramour to him slew herself with his sword for dole and sorrow.'

The meanwhile as this was a-doing, in came Merlin to King Mark and saw all this doing.

[1] as fast as he could
[2] in self-defence
[3] pitched, set up

'Here shall be,' said Merlin, 'in this same place the greatest battle betwixt two knights that ever was or ever shall be, and the truest lovers; and yet none of them shall slay the other.'

And there Merlin wrote their names upon the tomb with letters of gold, that shall fight in that place: which names was Lancelot du Lake and Tristram.

'Thou art a marvellous man,' said King Mark unto Merlin, 'that speakest of such marvels. Thou art a boisterous man and an unlikely [4] to tell of such deeds. What is thy name?' said King Mark.

'At this time,' said Merlin, 'I will not tell you. But at that time Sir Tristram is taken with his sovereign lady, then shall ye hear and know my name; and at that time ye shall hear tidings that shall not please you. Ah, Balin!' said Merlin, 'thou hast done thyself great hurt that thou saved not this lady that slew herself; for thou mightest have saved her an thou hadst would.'

'By the faith of my body,' said Balin, 'I might not save her, for she slew herself suddenly.'

'Me repenteth it,' [5] said Merlin; 'because of the death of that lady thou shalt strike a stroke most dolorous that ever man struck, except the stroke of Our Lord Jesus Christ. For thou shalt hurt the truest knight and the man of most worship that now liveth; and through that stroke three kingdoms shall be brought into great poverty, misery and wretchedness twelve year. And the knight shall not be whole of that wound many years.' Then Merlin took his leave.

'Nay,' said Balin, 'not so; for an I wist thou said sooth, I would do so perilous a deed that I would slay myself to make thee a liar.'

Therewith Merlin vanished away suddenly, and then Balin and his brother took their leave of King Mark.

'But first,' said the king, 'tell me your name.'

'Sir,' said Balan, 'ye may see he beareth two swords, and thereby ye may call him the Knight with the Two Swords.'

And so departed King Mark unto Camelot to King Arthur.

And Balin took the way to King Rions, and as they rode together they met with Merlin disguised so that they knew him nought.

'But whitherward ride ye?' said Merlin.

---

[4] it is rude and unseemly   [5] this distresses me

'We had little ado [6] to tell you,' said these two knights.

'But what is thy name?' said Balin.

'At this time,' said Merlin, 'I will not tell.'

'It is an evil sign,' said the knights, 'that thou art a true man, that [7] thou wilt not tell thy name.'

'As for that,' said Merlin, 'be as it be may. But I can tell you wherefore ye ride this way: for to meet with King Rions. But it will not avail you without ye have my counsel.'

'Ah,' said Balin, 'ye are Merlin! We will be ruled by your counsel!'

'Come on,' said Merlin, 'and ye shall have great worship. And look that ye do knightly, for ye shall have need.'

'As for that,' said Balin, 'dread you not, for we will do what we may.'

Then there lodged Merlin and these two knights in a wood among the leaves beside the highway, and took off the bridles of their horses and put them to grass, and laid them [8] down to rest till it was nigh midnight. Then Merlin bade them rise and make them ready: 'for here cometh the king nigh-hand, that was [9] stolen away from his host with a three score horses of his best knights, and twenty of them rode tofore the lord to warn the Lady de Vaunce that the king was coming.' For that night King Rions should have lain with her.

'Which is the king?' said Balin.

'Abide,' said Merlin, 'for here in a strait way ye shall meet with him.' And therewith he showed Balin and his brother the king.

And anon they met with him, and smote him down and wounded him freshly,[10] and laid him to the ground. And there they slew on the right hand and on the left hand more than forty of his men; and the remnant fled. Then went they again unto King Rions and would have slain him, had he not yielded him unto their grace. Then said he thus:

'Knights full of prowess, slay me not! For by my life ye may win, and by my death little.'

'Ye say sooth,' said the knights, and so laid him on a horse-litter.

[6] no reason

[7] it is a sign that you are not an honest man if

[8] themselves

[9] had

[10] grievously

So with that Merlin vanished, and came to King Arthur aforehand [11] and told him how his most enemy was taken and discomfit.[12]

'By whom?' said King Arthur.

'By two knights,' said Merlin, 'that would fain have your lordship. And to-morrow ye shall know what knights they are.'

So anon after came the Knight with the Two Swords and his brother, and brought with them King Rions of North Wales, and there delivered him to the porters, and charged them with him.[13]

And so they two returned again [14] in the dawning of the day.

Then King Arthur came to King Rions and said,

'Sir king, ye are welcome. By what adventure came ye hither?'

'Sir,' said King Rions, 'I came hither by a hard adventure.'

'Who won you?' said King Arthur.

'Sir,' said he, 'the Knight with the Two Swords and his brother, which are two marvellous knights of prowess.'

'I know them not,' said Arthur, 'but much am I beholding unto them.'

'Ah, sir,' said Merlin, 'I shall tell you. It is Balin that achieved the sword and his brother Balan, a good knight: there liveth not a better of prowess, nother of worthiness. And it shall be the greatest dole of him that ever I knew of knight; for he shall not long endure.'

'Alas,' said King Arthur, 'that is great pity; for I am much beholding unto him, and I have evil deserved it again for his kindness.' [15]

'Nay, nay,' said Merlin, 'he shall do much more for you, and that shall ye know in haste.'

. . . So within a day or two [16] King Arthur was somewhat sick, and he let pitch his pavilion in a meadow, and there he laid him down on a pallet to sleep; but he might have no

[11] in advance
[12] vanquished
[13] entrusted him to them
[14] went back
[15] I have not deserved that he should return kindness

[16] *Here M describes in some detail (O pp. 75–9) Arthur's attack on Nero, King Rions' brother. Arthur's brother-in-law, King Lot of Orkney, fights on Nero's side and is killed in battle.*

rest. Right so he heard a great noise of a horse, and therewith the king looked out at the porch door of the pavilion and saw a knight coming even [17] by him making great dole.

'Abide, fair sir,' said Arthur, 'and tell me wherefore thou makest this sorrow.'

'Ye may little amend [18] me,' said the knight, and so passed forth to the castle of Meliot.

And anon after that came Balin. And when he saw King Arthur he alight of his horse and came to the king on foot and salewed him. 'By my head,' said Arthur, 'ye be welcome. Sir, right now came riding this way a knight making great mourn, and for what cause I cannot tell. Wherefore I would desire of you of your courtesy and of your gentleness to fetch again that knight either by force either by his good will.'

'I shall do more for your lordship than that,' said Balin, 'other else I will grieve him.' [19]

So Balin rode more than a pace and found the knight with a damsel under a forest and said,

'Sir knight, ye must come with me unto King Arthur for to tell him of your sorrow.'

'That will I not,' said the knight, 'for it will harm me greatly and do you none avail.' [20]

'Sir,' said Balin, 'I pray you make you ready, for ye must go with me other else I must fight with you and bring you by force. And that were me loath to do.'

'Will ye be my warrant,' [1] said the knight, 'an I go with you?'

'Yea,' said Balin, 'other else, by the faith of my body, I will die therefore.'

And so he made him ready to go with Balin and left the damsel still. [2] And as they were even before [3] Arthur's pavilion, there came one invisible and smote the knight that went with Balin throughout the body with a spear.

'Alas!' said the knight, 'I am slain under your conduit [4] with a knight called Garlon. Therefore take my horse that is better

[17] close
[18] help
[19] and hurt him if need be
[20] no good

[1] protect me
[2] where she was
[3] close to
[4] protection

than yours, and ride to the damsel and follow the quest that I was in as she will lead you, and revenge my death when ye may.'

'That shall I do,' said Balin, 'and that [5] I make a vow to God and knighthood.'

And so he departed from King Arthur with great sorrow.

So King Arthur let bury this knight richly, and made mention on his tomb how here was slain Berbeus and by whom the treachery was done, of [6] the knight Garlon. But ever the damsel bore the truncheon [7] of the spear with her that Sir Harleus le Berbeus was slain withal.

So Balin and the damsel rode into the forest and there met with a knight that had been a-hunting. And that knight asked Balin for what cause he made so great sorrow.

'Me list not [8] to tell,' said Balin.

'Now,' said the knight, 'an I were armed as ye be, I would fight with you but if ye told me.'

'That should little need,' said Balin, 'I am not afeard to tell you,' and so told him all the case [9] how it was.

'Ah,' said the knight, 'is this all? Here I ensure you by the faith of my body never to depart from you while my life lasteth.'

And so they went to their ostry [10] and armed them and so rode forth with Balin. And as they came by an hermitage even [11] by a churchyard, there came Garlon invisible and smote this knight, Perin de Mount Beliard, throughout the body with a glaive.[12]

'Alas!' said the knight, 'I am slain by this traitor knight that rideth invisible.'

'Alas,' said Balin, 'this is not the first despite [13] that he hath done me!'

And there the hermit and Balin buried the knight under a rich [14] stone and a tomb royal. And on the morn they found letters of gold written how that Sir Gawain shall revenge his father's death, King Lot, on King Pellinor.

And anon after this Balin and the damsel rode forth till

[5] to do this
[6] by
[7] shaft
[8] I do not wish
[9] circumstances
[10] lodgings
[11] close
[12] spear
[13] wrong
[14] beautiful

they came to a castle. And anon Balin alight and went in.
And as soon as Balin came within the castle's gate the portcullis
were let down at his back, and there fell many men about the
damsel [15] and would have slain her. When Balin saw that, he
was sore grieved for he might not help her. But then he went
up into a tower and leapt over the walls into the ditch and
hurt not himself. And anon he pulled out his sword and
would have fought with them. And they all said nay, they
would not fight with him, for they did nothing but the old
custom of this castle, and told him that their lady was sick
and had lain many years, and she might not be whole but if
she had blood in a silver dish full, of a clean maid and a
king's daughter. 'And therefore the custom of this castle is
that there shall no damsel pass this way but she shall bleed
of her blood a silver dish full.'

'Well,' said Balin, 'she shall bleed as much as she may bleed,
but I will not lose the life of her while my life lasteth.'

And so Balin made her to bleed by her good will, but her
blood helped not the lady. And so she and he rested there
all that night and had good cheer, and in the morning they
passed on their ways. And as it telleth after in the *Sankgreall*,
that Sir Perceval his [16] sister helped that lady with her blood,
whereof she was dead.

Then they rode three or four days and never met with
adventure. And so by fortune they were lodged with a gentleman that was a rich man and well at ease. And as they
sat at supper Balin heard one complain grievously by him in
a chamber.

'What is this noise?' said Balin.

'Forsooth,' said his host, 'I will tell you. I was but late at
a jousting and there I jousted with a knight that is brother
unto King Pellam, and twice I smote him down. And then
he promised to quit me on [17] my best friend. And so he
wounded thus my son that cannot be whole till I have of that
knight's blood. And he rideth all invisible, but [18] I know not
his name.'

'Ah,' said Balin, 'I know that knight's name, which is
Garlon, and he hath slain two knights of mine in the same

---

[15] many men surrounded the
damsel
[16] Perceval's

[17] take his revenge upon
[18] and

manner. Therefore I had liefer meet with that knight than all the gold in this realm, for the despite he hath done me.'

'Well,' said his host, 'I shall tell you how. King Pellam of Listenoise hath made do cry in all the country a great feast that shall be within these twenty days, and no knight may come there but he bring his wife with him other his paramour. And that your enemy and mine ye shall see that day.'

'Then I promise you,' said Balin, 'part of his blood to heal your son withal.'

'Then we will be forward [19] to-morn,' said he.

So on the morn they rode all three toward King Pellam, and they had fifteen days' journey or they came thither. And that same day began the great feast. And so they alight and stabled their horses and went into the castle, but Balin's host might not be let in because he had no lady. But Balin was well received and brought unto a chamber and unarmed him. And there was brought him robes to his pleasure, and would have had Balin [20] leave his sword behind him.

'Nay,' said Balin, 'that will I not, for it is the custom of my country a knight [1] always to keep his weapon with him. Other else,' said he, 'I will depart as I came.'

Then they gave him leave with his sword,[2] and so he went into the castle and was among knights of worship, and his lady afore him. So after this Balin asked a knight and said,

'Is there not a knight in this court which his name [3] is Garlon?'

'Yes, sir, yonder he goeth, the knight with the black face, for he is the marvellest knight that is now living. And he destroyeth many good knights, for he goeth invisible.'

'Well,' said Balin, 'is that he?' Then Balin advised him [4] long, and thought: 'If I slay him here, I shall not escape. And if I leave him now, peradventure [5] I shall never meet with him again at such a steven,[6] and much harm he will do an he live.'

And therewith this Garlon espied that Balin visaged [7] him, so he came and slapped him on the face with the back of his hand and said,

[19] set off
[20] they wished Balin to
[1] for a knight
[2] to keep his sword
[3] whose name
[4] reflected
[5] perhaps
[6] occasion
[7] stared at

'Knight, why beholdest thou me so? For shame, eat thy
meat and do that [8] thou come for.'

'Thou sayest sooth,' said Balin, 'this is not the first spite [9]
that thou hast done me, and therefore I will do that I come
for.' And rose him up fiercely and clave his head to the
shoulders.

'Now give me the truncheon,' [10] said Balin to his lady,
'that he slew your knight with.'

And anon she gave it him, for always she bore the truncheon [10] with her. And therewith Balin smote him through
the body and said openly,

'With that truncheon thou slewest a good knight, and now
it sticketh in thy body.' Then Balin called unto his host and
said, 'Now may we fetch blood enough to heal your son
withal.'

So anon all the knights rose from the table for to set on
Balin. And King Pellam himself arose up fiercely and said,

'Knight, why hast thou slain my brother? Thou shalt die
therefore or thou depart.'

'Well,' said Balin, 'do it yourself.'

'Yes,' said King Pellam, 'there shall be no man have ado with
thee but I myself, for the love of my brother.'

Then King Pellam caught in his hand a grim [11] weapon and
smote eagerly at Balin, but he [12] put his sword betwixt his
head and the stroke, and therewith his sword brast in sunder.[13] And when Balin was weaponless [14] he ran into a
chamber for to seek a weapon, and from chamber to chamber,
and no weapon could he find. And always King Pellam followed after him. And at last he entered into a chamber which
was marvellously dight [15] and rich, and a bed arrayed [16] with
cloth of gold, the richest that might be, and one lying therein.
And thereby stood a table of clean gold with four pillars of

[8] what
[9] wrong
[10] shaft
[11] formidable. *According to F,
the 'grim weapon' was a great log
of wood.*
[12] Balin
[13] broke in two
[14] *Balin still had his other sword
with him, the one with which he
was to kill 'the man he loved
most in the world.' The fact is de-
liberately overlooked both in F
and in M because any reference to
it would have spoilt the motivation
of the Dolorous Stroke.*
[15] furnished
[16] covered

silver that bore up the table, and upon the table stood a
marvellous spear strangely [17] wrought.

So when Balin saw the spear he got it in his hand and
turned to King Pellam and felled him and smote him passingly sore with that spear, that [18] King Pellam fell down in a
swough. And therewith the castle broke, roof and walls, and
fell down to the earth. And Balin fell down and might not
stir hand nor foot, and for the most party of [19] that castle was
dead through the Dolorous Stroke.

Right so lay King Pellam and Balin three days.

Then Merlin came thither, and took up Balin and gat him
a good horse, for his was dead, and bade him void out of [20]
that country.

'Sir, I would have my damsel,' said Balin.

'Lo,' said Merlin, 'where she lieth dead.'

And King Pellam lay so many years sore wounded, and
might never be whole till that Galahad the Haut Prince
healed him in the quest of the Sankgreall. For in that place
was part of the blood of Our Lord Jesu Christ, which Joseph
of Arimathea brought into this land. And there himself lay
in that rich bed. And that was the spear which Longius
smote Our Lord with to the heart. And King Pellam was
nigh of Joseph his kin,[1] and that was the most worshipfullest
man on life in those days, and great pity it was of his hurt,
for through that stroke it turned to great dole, tray and teen.[2]

Then departed Balin from Merlin, 'for,'[3] he said, 'never
in this world we part neither meet no more.' So he rode
forth through the fair countries and cities and found the
people dead and slain on every side, and all that ever were
on life cried and said,

'Ah, Balin! Thou has done and caused great damage in these
countries! For the Dolorous Stroke thou gave unto King
Pellam these three countries are destroyed. And doubt not
but the vengeance will fall on thee at the last!'

But when Balin was past those countries he was passing
fain, and so he rode eight days or he met with many adven-

[17] wonderfully
[18] so that
[19] most of the people in
[20] leave

[1] close kin to Joseph
[2] suffering and sorrow
[3] and

ture.⁴ And at the last he came into a fair forest in a valley, and was ware of a tower. And there beside he met with a great horse tied to a tree, and beside there sat a fair knight on the ground and made great mourning, and he was a likely ⁵ man and a well made. Balin said,

'God you save! Why be ye so heavy? ⁶ Tell me, and I will amend, an I may, to my power.' ⁷

'Sir knight,' he said, 'thou dost me great grief, for I was in merry thoughts and thou puttest me to more pain.'

Then Balin went a little from him and looked on his horse; then heard Balin him say thus:

'Ah, fair lady! Why have ye broken my promise? For ye promised me to meet me here by noon. And I may curse you that ever ye gave me that sword, for with this sword I will slay myself,' and pulled it out.

And therewith came Balin and stert ⁸ unto him and took him by the hand.

'Let go my hand,' said the knight, 'or else I shall slay thee!'

'That shall not need,' said Balin, 'for I shall promise you my help to get you your lady an ye will tell me where she is.'

'What is your name?' said the knight.

'Sir, my name is Balin le Savage.'

'Ah, sir, I know you well enough: ye are the Knight with the Two Swords, and the man of most prowess of your hands living.'

'What is your name?' said Balin.

'My name is Garnish of the Mount, a poor man's son, and by ⁹ my prowess and hardiness ¹⁰ a duke made me knight and gave me lands. His name is Duke Harmel, and his daughter is she that I love, and she me, as I deemed.'

'How far is she hence?' said Balin.

'But six mile,' said the knight.

'Now ride we hence,' said these two knights.

So they rode more than a pace ¹¹ till that they came to a fair castle well walled and ditched.

'I will into the castle,' said Balin, 'and look if she be there.'

⁴ adventures
⁵ handsome
⁶ sad
⁷ as far as I am able

⁸ rushed
⁹ for
¹⁰ courage
¹¹ at a good speed

So he went in and searched from chamber to chamber, and found her bed, but she was not there. Then Balin looked into a fair little garden, and under a laurel tree he saw her lie upon a quilt of green samite,[12] and a knight in her arms, fast halsing either other,[13] and under their heads grass and herbs. When Balin saw her lie so with the foulest knight that ever he saw, and she a fair lady, then Balin went through all the chambers again, and told the knight how he found her as she had slept fast, and so brought him in the place where she lay fast sleeping.

And when Garnish beheld her so lying, for pure sorrow his mouth and nose burst out on-bleeding, and with his sword he smote off both their heads, and then he made sorrow out of measure, and said,

'O Balin! much sorrow has thou brought unto me, for hadst thou not showed me that sight I should have passed [14] my sorrow.'

'Forsooth,' said Balin, 'I did it to this intent that it should better thy courage,[15] and that ye might see and know her falsehood, and to cause you to leave love of such a lady; God knoweth I did none other but as I would ye did to me.'

'Alas!' said Garnish, 'now is my sorrow double that I may not [16] endure, now have I slain that I most loved in all my life!'

And therewith suddenly [17] he rove himself on [18] his own sword unto the hilts.

When Balin saw that, he dressed him [19] thenceward, lest folk would say he had slain them; and so he rode forth, and within three days he came by a cross, and thereon were letters of gold written, that said, IT IS NOT FOR NO KNIGHT ALONE TO RIDE TOWARD THIS CASTLE. Then saw he an old hoar gentleman coming toward him, that said,

'Balin le Savage, thou passest thy bounds to come this way, therefore turn again [20] and it will avail thee.' And he vanished away anon.

And so he heard an horn blow as it had been the death of

---

12 rich silk
13 each other
14 I should have been spared
15 strengthen your resolution
16 and too great for me to
17 swiftly
18 ran upon
19 went
20 back

a beast. 'That blast,' said Balin, 'is blown for me, for I am
the prize and yet am I not dead.' Annon withal he saw an
hundred ladies and many knights that welcomed him with fair
semblaunt,[1] and made him passing good cheer unto his sight,[2]
and led him into the castle, and there was dancing and
ministrelsy and all manner of joy. Then the chief lady of the
castle said,

'Knight with the Two Swords, ye must have ado and joust
with a knight hereby that keepeth an island, for there may no
man pass this way but he must joust or he pass.'

'That is an unhappy custom,' said Balin, 'that a knight may
not pass this way but if he joust.'

'Ye shall not have ado but with one knight,' said the lady.

'Well,' said Balin, 'syn I shall, thereto I am ready; but
travelling men are oft weary and their horses too, but though
my horse be weary my heart is not weary. I would be fain
there my death should be.'[3]

'Sir,' said a knight to Balin, 'methinketh your shield is not
good, I will lend you a bigger, thereof I pray you.'

And so he took the shield that was unknown and left his
own, and so rode unto the island, and put him and his horse
in a great boat. And when he came on the other side he met
with a damsel, and she said,

'O knight Balin, why have ye left your own shield? Alas!
ye have put yourself in great danger, for by your shield ye
should have been known. It is great pity of you as ever was of
knight, for of [4] thy prowess and hardiness thou hast no fellow
living.'

'Me repenteth,' said Balin, 'that ever I came within this
country, but I may not turn now again [5] for shame, and what
adventure shall fall to me, be it life or death, I will take the
adventure that shall come to me.'

And then he looked on his armour and understood he was
well armed, and therewith blessed him [6] and mounted upon

---

[1] received him with pleasant
looks
[2] showed him great welcome
[3] even though I should find
death

[4] as to
[5] back
[6] crossed himself

his horse. Then afore him he saw come riding out of a castle a knight, and his horse trapped all red,[7] and himself in the same colour. When this knight in the red beheld Balin, him thought it should be his brother Balin because of his two swords,[8] but because he knew not his shield he deemed it was not he.

And so they aventred [9] their spears and came marvellously fast together, and they smote other [10] in the shields, but their spears and their course [11] were so big [12] that it bare down horse and man, that they lay both in a swoon; but Balin was bruised sore with the fall of his horse, for he was weary of travel. And Balan was the first that rose on foot and drew his sword, and went toward Balin, and he arose and went against him; but Balan smote Balin first, and he put up his shield and smote him through the shield and tamed [13] his helm. Then Balin smote him again [14] with that unhappy sword, and well-nigh had felled his brother Balan, and so they fought there together till their breaths failed.

Then Balin looked up to the castle and saw the towers stand full of ladies. So they went unto battle again, and wounded everych other dolefully, and then they breathed ofttimes, and so went unto battle that all the place thereas [15] they fought was blood red. And at that time there was none of them both but they had either smitten other seven great wounds, so that the least of them might have been the death of the mightiest giant in this world.

Then they went to battle again so marvellously that doubt [16] it was to hear of that battle for the great blood-shedding, and their hauberks unnailed,[17] that naked they were on every side. At the last Balan, the younger brother, withdrew him a little and laid him down. Then said Balin le Savage,

[7] in red trappings

[8] *Balin had only one sword left. 'Because of his two swords' is a misreading of 'chelui a deus espees' ('quant il voit chelui a deus espees') used in F as a proper name.*

[9] levelled. *Possibly a corruption of* afeautryd, *'set.'*

[10] each other

[11] coming together

[12] strong

[13] split

[14] back

[15] where

[16] a fearful thing

[17] their coats of mail fell apart

'What knight art thou? For or now I [18] found never no knight that matched me.'

'My name is,' said he, 'Balan, brother unto the good knight Balin.'

'Alas,' said Balin, 'that ever I should see this day!' and therewith he fell backward in a swoon.

Then Balan yode on all four, feet and hands, and put off the helm of his brother, and might not know him by the visage, it was so full hewn and bled; but when he awoke he said,

'O Balan, my brother! Thou hast slain me and I thee, wherefore all the wide world shall speak of us both.'

'Alas,' said Balin, 'that ever I saw this day, that through mishap I might not know you! For I espied well your two swords,[19] but because ye had another shield I deemed ye had been another knight.'

'Alas,' said Balin, 'all that made an unhappy knight [20] in the castle, for he caused me to leave mine own shield to our both's destruction. And if I might live I would destroy that castle for ill customs.'

'That were [1] well done,' said Balan, 'for I had never grace [2] to depart from them syn that I came hither, for here it happed me to slay a knight that kept this island, and syn might I never depart. And no more should ye, brother, an ye might have slain me as ye have and escaped yourself with the life.'

Right so came the lady of the tower with four knights and six ladies and six yeomen unto them, and there she heard how they made their moan either to other and said, 'We came both out of one womb, that is to say one mother's belly, and so shall we lie both in one pit.' So Balan prayed the lady of her gentleness for his true service that she would bury them both in that same place there the battle was done, and she granted them, with weeping, it should be done richly in the best manner.

'Now, will ye send for a priest, that we may receive our

---

[18] until now I have
[19] *See above, note 8.*
[20] all this was done by an unlucky knight

[1] would have been
[2] the good fortune

sacrament, and receive the blessed body of Our Lord Jesu Christ?'

'Yea,' said the lady, 'it shall be done;' and so she sent for a priest and gave [3] them their rites.

'Now,' said Balin, 'when we are buried in one tomb, and the mention made over us how two brethren slew each other, there will never good knight nor good man see our tomb but they will pray for our souls.' And so all the ladies and gentlewomen wept for pity.

Then anon Balan died, but Balin died not till the midnight after. And so were they buried both, and the lady let make a mention of Balan how he was there slain by his brother's hands, but she knew not Balin's name.

In the morn came Merlin and let write Balin's name on the tomb with letters of gold, that HERE LIETH BALIN LE SAVAGE THAT WAS THE KNIGHT WITH THE TWO SWORDS, AND HE THAT SMOTE THE DOLOROUS STROKE. Also Merlin let make there a bed, that there should never man lie therein but he went out of his wit. Yet Lancelot du Lake fordid [4] that bed through his noblesse.[5]

And anon after Balin was dead Merlin took his sword and took off the pommel and set on another pommel. So Merlin bade a knight that stood before him to handle the sword, and he essayed it and might not handle it. Then Merlin laughed.

'Why laugh ye?' said the knight.

'This is the cause,' said Merlin: 'there shall never man handle this sword but the best knight of the world, and that shall be Sir Lancelot other else Galahad, his son. And Lancelot with this sword shall slay the man that in the world he loveth best, that shall be Sir Gawain.'

And all this he let write in the pommel of the sword.

Then Merlin let make a bridge of iron and of steel into that island, and it was but half a foot broad, 'and there shall never man pass that bridge, nother have hardiness [6] to go over it but if he were a passing good man and a good knight without treachery or villainy.' Also the scabbard of Balin's sword Merlin left it on this side the island, that Galahad should find

---

[3] he gave
[4] destroyed. *The spell was to be broken by Lancelot's ring.*
[5] valour
[6] courage

it. Also Merlin let make by his subtlety [7] that Balin's sword was put in a marble stone standing upright as great as a millstone, and hoved [8] always above the water, and did many years. And so by adventure it swam down the stream to the City of Camelot, that is in English called Winchester.[9] And the same day Galahad the Haute Prince came with King Arthur, and so Galahad brought with him the scabbard and achieved the sword that was in the marble stone hoving upon the water. And on Whitsunday he achieved the sword, as it is rehearsed in *The Book of the Sankgreall.*

Soon after this was done Merlin came to King Arthur and told him of the Dolorous Stroke that Balin gave King Pellam, and how Balin and Balan fought together the marvellest battle that ever was heard of, and how they were buried both in one tomb.

'Alas!' said King Arthur, 'this is the greatest pity that ever I heard tell of two knights, for in this world I knew never such two knights.'

THUS ENDETH THE TALE OF BALIN AND OF BALAN, TWO BRETHREN THAT WERE BORN IN NORTHUMBERLAND, THAT WERE PASSING GOOD KNIGHTS AS EVER WERE IN THOSE DAYS.

[7] cunning
[8] rose

[9] *See below,* The Fair Maid of Astolat, *note 1.*

Pelleas and Ettard

Now will we begin at Sir Gawain that held that way till
that he came to a fair manor where dwelled an old knight and
a good householder. And there Sir Gawain asked the knight
if he knew of any adventures.

'I shall show you to-morn,' said the knight, 'marvellous
adventures.'

So on the morn they rode all in same [1] to the Forest of
Adventures till they came to a laund,[2] and thereby they found
a cross. And as they stood and hoved,[3] there came by them
the fairest knight and the seemliest [4] man that ever they saw,
but he made the greatest dole that ever man made. And then
he was ware of Sir Gawain and salewed him, and prayed to
God to send him much worship.

'As for that,' said Sir Gawain, 'gramercy. Also I pray to
God send you honour and worship.'

'Ah,' said the knight, 'I may lay that on side,[5] for sorrow
and shame cometh unto me after worship.'

And therewith he passed unto that one side of the laund,[2]
and on that other side saw Sir Gawain ten knights that
hoved [3] and made them ready with their shields and with
their spears against that one knight that came by Sir Gawain.
Then this one knight feautred [6] a great spear, and one of the
knights encountered with him. But this woeful knight smote
him so hard that he fell over his horse [7] tail. So this dolorous
knight served them all, that at the leastway [8] he smote down

1 together
2 glade
3 waited
4 handsomest

5 I can dispense with that
6 fixed in its rest
7 horse's
8 leastways

horse and man, and all he did with one spear. And so when
they were all ten on foot they went to the one knight, and
he stood stone-still and suffered them to pull him down off his
horse, and bound him hand and foot, and tied him under the
horse [7] belly, and so led him with them.

'Ah, Jesu,' said Sir Gawain, 'this is a doleful sight to see the
yonder knight so to be entreated! And it seemeth by the
knight that he suffereth them to bind him so, for he maketh
no resistance.'

'No,' said the host, 'that is truth, for, an he would, they
all were [9] too weak for him.'

'Sir,' said the damsel [10] unto Sir Gawain, 'meseemeth it were
your worship to help that dolorous knight, for methinketh
he is one of the best knights that ever I saw.'

'I would do for him,' [11] said Sir Gawain, 'but it seemeth he
would have no help.'

'No,' said the damsel, 'methinketh ye have no list [12] to help
him.'

Thus as they talked they saw a knight on the other side of
the laund [13] all armed save the head. And on the other side
there came a dwarf on horseback all armed save the head, with
a great mouth and a short nose. And when the dwarf came
nigh he said,

'Where is this lady should meet us here?'

And therewithal she came forth out of the wood. And then
they began to strive for the lady, for the knight said he would
have her.

'Will we do well?' [14] said the dwarf. 'Yonder is a knight at
the cross. Let it be put upon [15] him, and as he deemeth it,
so shall it be.'

'I will well,' said the knight.

And so they went all three unto Sir Gawain and told him
wherefore they strove.

'Well, sirs, will ye put the matter in mine hand?'

[9] would be
[10] *One of the three damsels
whom Gawain, Ywain and Mar-
halt met while they were waiting
for 'any of the errant knights
to teach them unto strange adventures'* (O, *p. 162*).

[11] would willingly help him
[12] desire
[13] glade
[14] shall we do the right thing?
[15] entrusted to

'Yea, sir,' they said both.

'Now, damsel,' said Sir Gawain, 'ye shall stand betwixt them both, and whither [16] ye list better [17] to go to he shall have you.'

And when she was set between them both she left the knight and went to the dwarf. And then the dwarf took her up and went his way singing, and the knight went his way with great mourning.

Then came there two knights all armed and cried on hight,

'Sir Gawain, knight of the court of King Arthur! Make thee ready in haste and joust with me!'

So they ran together, that either [18] fell down. And then on foot they drew their swords and did full actually.[19] The meanwhile the other knight went to the damsel [20] and asked her why she abode with that knight, and said,

'If ye would abide with me I would be your faithful knight.'

'And with you will I be,' said the damsel, 'for I may not find in my heart to be with him, for right now here was one knight that scomfited [1] ten knights, and at the last he was cowardly led away. And therefore let us two go [2] while they fight.'

And Sir Gawain fought with that other knight long, but at the last they accorded both.[3] And then the knight prayed Sir Gawain to lodge with him that night. So as Sir Gawain went with this knight he said,

'What knight is he in this country that smote down the ten knights? For [4] when he had done so manfully he suffered them to bind him hand and foot, and so led [5] him away.'

'Ah,' said the knight, 'that is the best knight, I trow, in the world, and the most man of prowess. And it is the greatest pity of him as of any knight living, for he hath been served so as he was at this time more than ten times. And his name

---

[16] to whichever one
[17] prefer
[18] with such force that both
[19] fought vigorously
[20] *i.e. the one who accompanied Gawain*
[1] defeated

[2] *The damsel considers Gawain unworthy of her company because he has allowed the knight to be ill-treated in his presence.*
[3] were reconciled
[4] And
[5] they led

hight Sir Pelleas; and he loveth a great lady in this country, and her name is Ettard. And so when he loved her there was [6] cried in this country a great jousts three days,[7] and all these knights of this country were there and gentlewomen. And who that proved him the best knight should have a passing good sword and a circlet of gold, and that circlet the knight should give it to the fairest lady that was at that jousts.

'And this knight Sir Pelleas was far the best of any that was there, and there were five hundred knights, but there was never man that ever Sir Pelleas met but he struck him down, other else from his horse,[8] and every day of three days he struck down twenty knights. And therefore they gave him the prize. And forthwithal he went thereas [9] the lady Ettard was and gave her the circlet and said openly she was the fairest lady that there was, and that would he prove upon any knight that would say nay.

'And so he chose her for his sovereign lady, and never to love other but her. But she was so proud that she had scorn of him and said she would never love him though he would die for her; wherefore all ladies and gentlewomen had scorn of her that [10] she was so proud, for there were fairer than she, and there was none that was there but an Sir Pelleas would have proffered them love they would have showed him the same for his noble prowess. And so this knight promised Ettard to follow her into this country and never to leave her till she loved him, and thus he is here the most party nigh her and lodged by a priory.

'And every week she sendeth knights to fight with him, and when he hath put them to the worse, then will he suffer them wilfully [11] to take him prisoner because he would have a sight of this lady. And always she doth him great despite,[12] for sometimes she maketh his knights to tie him to his horse [13] tail, and sometime bind him under the horse [13] belly. Thus in the most shamefullest wise that she can think he is brought to her, and all she doth it for to [14] cause him to leave this country

---

[6] and so he loved her; and then was

[7] a great tournament which was to last three days

[8] or unhorsed him

[9] where

[10] because

[11] voluntarily

[12] she scorns him

[13] horse's

[14] all this she does in order to

and to leave his loving. But all this cannot make him to leave, for an he would have fought on foot he might have had the better of the ten knights as well on foot as on horse-back.'

'Alas,' said Sir Gawain, 'it is great pity of him, and after this night I will seek him to-morrow in this forest to do him all the help I can.'

So on the morrow Sir Gawain took his leave of his host, Sir Carados, and rode into the forest. And at the last he met with Sir Pelleas making great moan out of measure; so each of them salewed other, and asked [15] him why he made such sorrow. And as it above rehearseth Sir Pelleas told Sir Gawain:

'But always I suffer her knights to fare so with me as ye saw yesterday, in trust at the last to win her love; for she knoweth well all her knights should not lightly win me an me list [16] to fight with them to the uttermost. Wherefore an I loved her not so sore I had liefer die an hundred times, an I might die so oft, rather than I would suffer that despite,[17] but I trust she will have pity upon me at the last; for love causeth many a good knight to suffer to have his intent,[18] but alas, I am unfortunate!' And therewith he made so great dole that unnethe [19] he might hold him on his horse [20] back.

'Now,' said Sir Gawain, 'leave your mourning, and I shall promise you by the faith of my body to do all that lieth in my power to get you the love of your lady, and thereto I will plight you my troth.'

'Ah,' said Sir Pelleas, 'of what court are ye?'

'Sir, I am of the court of King Arthur, and his sister son, and King Lot of Orkney was my father, and my name is Sir Gawain.'

'And my name is Sir Pelleas, born in the Isles, and of many Isles I am lord. And never loved I lady nother damsel till now. And, sir knight, since ye are so nigh cousin unto King Arthur and are a king's son, therefore betray me not, but help me, for I may never come by her but by some good knight. For she is in a strong castle here fast by, within this four mile, and over all this country she is lady of.

---

[15] Gawain asked
[16] if I wished
[17] scorn

[18] the object of his desire
[19] hardly
[20] horse's

'And so I may never come to her presence but as [1] I suffer her knights to take me, and but if I did so that I might have a sight of her, I had been dead long or this time.[2] And yet fair word had I never none of her. But when I am brought tofore her she rebuketh me in the foulest manner; and then they take me my horse and harness and putteth me out of the gates, and she will not suffer me to eat nother drink. And always I offer me to be her prisoner, but that will she not suffer [3] me; for I would desire no more, what pains that ever I had, so that I might have a sight of her daily.'

'Well,' said Sir Gawain, 'all this shall I amend, an ye will do as I shall devise. I will have your armour, and so will I ride unto her castle and tell her that I have slain you, and so shall I come within her to cause her to cherish me.[4] And then shall I do my true part,[5] that ye shall not fail to have the love of her.'

And there, when Sir Gawain plight his troth unto Sir Pelleas to be true and faithful unto him, so each one plight their troth to other, and so they changed horse and harness. And Sir Gawain departed and came to the castle where stood her pavilions without the gate. And as soon as Ettard had espied Sir Gawain she fled toward the castle. But Sir Gawain spake on hight [6] and bade her abide, for he was not Sir Pelleas:

'I am another knight that have slain Sir Pelleas.'

'Then do off your helm,' said the lady Ettard, 'that I may see your visage.'

So when she saw that it was not Sir Pelleas she made him alight and led him into her castle and asked him faithfully whether he had slain Sir Pelleas, and he said yea. Then he told her his name was Sir Gawain, of the court of King Arthur, and his sister's son, and how he had slain Sir Pelleas.

'Truly,' said she, 'that is great pity for he was a passing good knight of his body.[7] But of all men on life I hated him most, for I could never be quit [8] of him. And for ye have slain him I shall be your woman and to do anything that may please you.'

[1] unless
[2] and had I not done this so that I might have sight of her I should have died long since
[3] allow
[4] go into the place where she lives and earn her esteem
[5] duty
[6] loudly
[7] a good and strong knight
[8] rid

So she made Sir Gawain good ˙cheer. Then Sir Gawain said that he loved a lady and by no mean she would love him.

'She is to blame,' said Ettard, 'an she will not love you, for ye that be so well-born a man and such a man of prowess, there is no lady in this world too good for you.'

'Will ye,' said Sir Gawain, 'promise me to do what that ye may do, by the faith of your body,[9] to get me the love of my lady?'

'Yea, sir, and that I promise you by my faith.'

'Now,' said Sir Gawain, 'it is yourself that I love so well, therefore hold your promise.'

'I may not choose,' said the lady Ettard, 'but if [10] I should be forsworn.'

And so she granted him to fulfil all his desire.

So it was in the month of May that she and Sir Gawain went out of the castle and supped in a pavilion, and there was made a bed, and there Sir Gawain and Ettard went to bed together. And in another pavilion she laid her damsels, and in the third pavilion she laid part of her knights, for then she had no dread of Sir Pelleas. And there Sir Gawain lay with her in the pavilion two days and two nights.

And on the third day on the morn early Sir Pelleas armed him, for he had never slept since Sir Gawain departed from him, for Sir Gawain promised him by the faith of his body [9] to come to him unto his pavilion by the priory within the space of a day and a night. Then Sir Pelleas mounted upon horseback and came to the pavilions that stood without the castle, and found in the first pavilion three knights in three beds, and three squires lying at their feet. Then went he to the second pavilion and found four gentlewomen lying in four beds. And then he yode to the third pavilion and found Sir Gawain lying in the bed with his lady Ettard and either clipping [11] other in arms. And when he saw that, his heart well-nigh brast for sorrow, and said, 'Alas, that ever a knight should be found so false!'

And then he took his horse and might not abide no longer for pure sorrow, and when he had ridden nigh half a mile he turned again and thought for to slay them both. And when

---

[9] your (his) faith　　　　　　[11] embracing
[10] or else

he saw them lie so both sleeping fast that unnethe he might [12] hold him on horseback for sorrow, and said thus to himself: 'Though this knight be never [13] so false, I will never slay him sleeping, for I will never destroy the high Order of Knighthood,' and therewith he departed again. And or [14] he had ridden half a mile he returned again and thought then to slay them both, making the greatest sorrow that ever man made. And when he came to the pavilions he tied his horse to a tree and pulled out his sword naked in his hand and went to them thereas [15] they lay. And yet he thought shame to slay them, and laid the naked sword overthwart [16] both their throats, and so took his horse and rode his way.

And when Sir Pelleas came to his pavilions he told his knights and his squires how he had sped, and said thus unto them:

'For your good and true service ye have done me I shall give you all my goods, for I will go unto my bed and never arise till I be dead. And when that I am dead, I charge [17] you that ye take the heart out of my body and bear it her betwixt two silver dishes and tell her how I saw her lie with that false knight Sir Gawain.'

Right so Sir Pelleas unarmed himself and went unto his bed making marvellous [18] dole and sorrow.

Then Sir Gawain and Ettard awoke of their sleep and found the naked sword overthwart [16] their throats. Then she knew it was the sword of Sir Pelleas.

'Alas!' she said, 'Sir Gawain, ye have betrayed Sir Pelleas and me, for you told me you had slain him, and now I know well it is not so: he is on life. But had he been so uncourteous unto you as ye have been to him, ye had been a dead knight. But ye have deceived me that [19] all ladies and damsels may beware by you and me.'

And therewith Sir Gawain made him ready and went into the forest.

So it happed the Damsel of the Lake, Ninive, met with a

[12] he could hardly
[13] ever
[14] But before
[15] where

[16] across
[17] command
[18] great
[19] in such a way that

knight of Sir Pelleas that went on his foot [20] in this forest making great dole, and she asked him the cause; and so the woeful knight told her all how his master and lord was betrayed through a knight and a lady, and how he will never arise out of his bed till he be dead.

'Bring me to him,' said she anon, 'and I will warrant his life. He shall not die for love, and she that hath caused him so to love she shall be in as evil plight as he is or it be long to,[1] for it is no joy of such a proud lady that will not have no mercy of such a valiant knight.'

Anon that knight brought her unto him, and when she saw him lie on his bed she thought she saw never so likely [2] a knight. And therewith she threw an enchantment upon him, and he fell on sleep. And then she rode unto the lady Ettard, and charged [3] that no man should awake him till she came again.[4] So within two hours she brought the lady Ettard thither, and both the ladies found him on sleep.

'Lo,' said the Damsel of the Lake, 'ye ought to be ashamed for to murder such a knight,' and therewith she threw such an enchantment upon her that she loved him so sore that wellnigh she was near out of her mind.

'Ah, Lord Jesu,' said this lady Ettard, 'how is it befallen unto me that I love now that [5] I have hated most of any man on life?'

'That is the righteous judgment of God,' said the damsel.

And then anon Sir Pelleas awaked and looked upon Ettard, and when he saw her he knew her, and then he hated her more than any woman on life, and said,

'Away, traitress, and come never in my sight!'

And when she heard him say so she wept and made great sorrow out of mind.[6]

'Sir knight Pelleas,' said the Damsel of the Lake, 'take your horse and come forth without of this country, and ye shall love a lady that will love you.'

'I will well,' said Sir Pelleas, 'for this lady Ettard hath done

---

[20] on foot
[1] before long
[2] handsome
[3] gave orders

[4] back
[5] him whom
[6] beyond measure (*Fr.: raison*)

me great despite [7] and shame;' and there he told her the
beginning and ending, and how he had never purposed to
have risen again till he had been dead. 'And now such grace
God hath sent me that I hate her as much as I have loved her.'

'Thank me therefor,' said the Lady of the Lake.

Anon Sir Pelleas armed him and took his horse and commanded his men to bring after [8] his pavilions and his stuff
where the Lady of the Lake would assign them. So this lady
Ettard died for sorrow, and the Damsel of the Lake rejoiced
Sir Pelleas, and loved together during their life.

[7] wrong   [8] follow him with

The Knight of the Cart

And thus it passed on from Candlemas until after Easter, that [1] the month of May was come, when every lusty [2] heart beginneth to blossom and to burgeon. For, like as trees and herbs burgeoneth and flourisheth in May, in like wise every lusty [2] heart that is any manner of lover springeth,[3] burgeoneth, buddeth and flourisheth in lusty [2] deeds. For it giveth unto all lovers courage,[4] that lusty [2] month of May, in some thing [5] to constrain him to [6] some manner of thing, more than in any other month, for divers causes: for then all herbs and trees reneweth a man and woman, and in like wise lovers calleth to their mind old gentleness [7] and old service, and many kind deeds that was forgotten by negligence.

For like as winter rasure [8] doth alway erase [9] and deface green summer, so fareth it by unstable love in man and woman, for in many persons there is no stability: for we may see all [10] day, for a little blast of winter's rasure,[8] anon we shall deface and lay apart [11] true love, for little or nought, that cost much thing.[12] This is no wisdom nother no stability, but it is feebleness of nature and great disworship,[13] whosoever useth this.

Therefore, like as May month flowereth and flourisheth in every man's garden, so in like wise let every man of worship flourish his heart in this world; first unto God, and next unto

[1] so that
[2] merry
[3] breaks forth
[4] desire
[5] for certain things
[6] to exert oneself in
[7] courtesy

[8] biting wind
[9] demolish
[10] every
[11] discard
[12] that is so precious
[13] disgrace

the joy of them that he promised his faith unto; for there was
never worshipful man nor worshipful woman but they loved
one better than another; and worship in arms may never be
foiled.[14] But first reserve the honour to God, and secondly
thy quarrel must come of [15] thy lady. And such love I call
virtuous love.

But nowadays men cannot love seven night but they must
have all their desires. That love may not endure by reason,
for where they be soon accorded and hasty,[16] heat soon cool-
eth. And right so fareth the love nowadays, soon hot, soon
cold. This is no stability. But the old love was not so; for
men and women could love together seven years, and no
lecherous lusts [17] was betwixt them, and then was love truth
and faithfulness. And so in like wise was used such love in
King Arthur's days.

Wherefore I liken love nowadays unto summer and winter:
for, like as the one is cold and the other is hot, so fareth love
nowadays. And therefore all ye that be lovers, call unto your
remembrance the month of May, like as did Queen Guinevere,
for whom I make here a little mention, that [18] while she lived
she was a true lover, and therefore she had a good end.

So it befell in the month of May, Queen Guinevere called
unto her ten knights of the Table Round, and she gave them
warning that early upon the morn she would ride on-maying
into woods and fields besides Westminster.

'And I warn you that there be none of you but he be well
horsed, and that ye all be clothed all in green, either in silk
other in cloth. And I shall bring with me ten ladies, and every
knight shall have a lady by him. And every knight shall have
a squire and two yeomen; and I will that all be well horsed.'

So they made them ready in the freshest [19] manner, and
these were the names of the knights: Sir Kay le Seneschal, Sir
Agravain, Sir Braundiles, Sir Sagramore le Desirous, Sir Dodinas le Savage, Sir Ozanna le Cure Hardy, Sir Ladinas of the
Forest Savage, Sir Persaunt of Inde, Sir Ironside, that was
called the Knight of the Red Launds, and Sir Pelleas the

[14] cast down
[15] must be for the sake of
[16] when such desires are quickly
and hastily fulfilled
[17] pleasures
[18] because
[19] gayest

Lover. And these ten knights made them ready in the freshest [19] manner to ride with the queen.

And so upon the morn or it were day, in a May morning,
they took their horses with the queen, and rode on-maying in
woods and meadows as it pleased them, in great joy and de-
lights. For the queen had cast [20] to have been again with King
Arthur at the furthest by ten of the clock, and so [1] was that
time her purpose.

Then there was a knight which hight Sir Mellyagaunce,
and he was son unto King Bagdemagus, and this knight had
that time a castle of the gift of King Arthur within seven mile
of Westminster. And this knight Sir Mellyagaunce loved
passingly well Queen Guinevere, and so had he done long
and many years. And the book saith he had lain in await [2] for
to steal away the queen, but evermore he forbare for because
of Sir Lancelot; for in no wise he would meddle with the
queen an Sir Lancelot were in her company other else an he
were near-hand.

And that time was such a custom that the queen rode never
without a great fellowship of men of arms about her. And
they were many good knights, and the most party [3] were
young men that would have worship,[4] and they were called
the Queen's Knights. And never in no battle, tournament
nother jousts they bare none of them no manner of knowledging of their own arms but [5] plain white shields, and thereby
they were called the Queen's Knights. And when it happed
any of them to be of great worship by his noble deeds, then
at the next feast of Pentecost, if there were any slain or dead
(as there was none year that there failed but there were some
dead), then was there chosen in his stead that was dead the
most men of worship that were called the Queen's Knights.
And thus they came up first, or [6] they were renowned men
of worship, both Sir Lancelot and all the remnant of them.

But this knight Sir Mellyagaunce had espied the queen well
and her purpose, and how Sir Lancelot was not with her, and

[20] intended
[1] such
[2] ambush
[3] most of them

[4] wished to distinguish themselves
[5] bore no arms by which they
could be recognized, but only
[6] before

how she had no men of arms with her but the ten noble knights all rayed [7] in green for maying. Then he purveyed him [8] a twenty men of arms and an hundred archers for to distress the queen and her knights; for he thought that time was best season to take the queen.

So as the queen was out on-maying with all her knights, which were bedashed [9] with herbs, mosses and flowers in the freshest [10] manner, right so there came out of a wood Sir Mellyagaunce with an eight score men, all harnessed as they should fight in a battle of arrest, [11] and bade the queen and her knights abide, for maugre their heads [12] they should abide.

'Traitor knight,' said Queen Guinevere, 'what cast [13] thou to do? Wilt thou shame thyself? Bethink thee how thou art a king's son, and a knight of the Table Round, and thou thus to be about to dishonour the noble king that made thee knight! Thou shamest all knighthood and thyself and me. And I let thee wit thou shalt never shame me, for I had liefer cut mine own throat in twain rather than thou should dishonour me!'

'As for all this language,' said Sir Mellyagaunce, 'be as it be may. For wit you well, madam, I have loved you many a year, and never or now could I get you at such avail. [14] And therefore I will take you as I find you.'

Then spake all the ten noble knights at once and said,

'Sir Mellyagaunce, wit thou well thou art about to jeopardy thy worship to dishonour, [15] and also ye cast [16] to jeopardy your persons. Howbeit we be unarmed and ye have us at a great advantage, for it seemeth by you that ye have laid watch upon us, but rather than ye should put the queen to a shame and us all, we had as lief to depart from our lives, for an we otherways did we were shamed forever.'

Then said Sir Mellyagaunce:

'Dress [17] you as well ye can, and keep the queen!'

Then the ten knights of the Round Table drew their swords and these other let run at them with their spears. And the ten knights manly abode [18] them, and smote away their spears, that no spear did them no harm. Then they lashed together

[7] dressed	[13] mean
[8] chose	[14] advantage
[9] adorned	[15] put your honour in jeopardy
[10] gayest	[16] propose
[11] fight for capture	[17] prepare
[12] whether they wished it or not	[18] withstood

with swords, and anon Sir Kay, Sir Sagramore, Sir Agravain, Sir Dodinas, Sir Ladinas, and Sir Ozanna were smitten to the earth with grimly wounds. Then Sir Braundiles and Sir Persaunt, Sir Ironside, and Sir Pelleas fought long, and they were sore wounded, for these ten knights, or ever they were laid to the ground, slew forty men of the boldest and the best of them.

So when the queen saw her knights thus dolefully wounded and needs must be slain at the last, then for very pity and sorrow she cried and said,

'Sir Mellyagaunce, slay not my noble knights, and I will go with thee upon this covenant: that thou save them and suffer them no more to be hurt, with this [19] that they be led with me wheresomever thou leadest me. For I will rather slay myself than I will go with thee, unless that these noble knights may be in my presence.'

'Madam,' said Sir Mellyagaunce, 'for your sake they shall be led with you into mine own castle, with that [20] ye will be ruled [1] and ride with me.'

Then the queen prayed the four knights to leave their fighting, and [2] she and they would not depart.[3]

'Madam,' said Sir Pelleas, 'we will do as ye do, for as for me I take no force of my life nor death.' [4]

For, as the French book saith, Sir Pelleas gave such buffets there that none armour might hold him.

Then by the queen's commandment they left battle and dressed [5] the wounded knights on horseback, some sitting and some overthwart their horses, that it was pity to behold. And then Sir Mellyagaunce charged the queen and all her knights that none of all her fellowship should depart from her, for full sore he dread Sir Lancelot du Lake, lest he should have any knowledging.[6] And all this espied the queen, and privily she called unto her a child [7] of her chamber which was swiftly horsed of a great advantage.[8]

'Now go thou,' said she, 'when thou seest thy time, and bear

---

[19] on this condition
[20] provided that
[1] submit
[2] and [said that]
[3] part
[4] it matters not whether I live or die

[5] lifted
[6] lest this should come to his knowledge
[7] young nobleman
[8] mounted on a good horse

this ring unto Sir Lancelot du Lake, and pray him as he loveth me that he will see me and rescue me, if ever he will have joy of me. And spare not thy horse,' said the queen, 'nother for water nother for land.'

So the child [7] espied his time, and lightly [9] he took his horse with spurs and departed as fast he might. And when Sir Mellyagaunce saw him so flee, he understood that it was by the queen's commandment for to warn Sir Lancelot. Then they that were best horsed chased him and shot at him, but from them all the child [7] went deliverly.[10]

And then Sir Mellyagaunce said unto the queen,

'Madam, ye are about to betray me, but I shall ordain for Sir Lancelot that he shall not come lightly [9] at you.'

And then he rode with her and all the fellowship in all the haste that they might. And so by the way Sir Mellyagaunce laid in bushment [11] of the best archers that he might get in his country, to the number of a thirty, to await upon Sir Lancelot, charging [12] them that if they saw such a manner a knight come by the way upon a white horse, 'that in any wise ye slay his horse, but in no manner have ye ado with him bodily, for he is overhardy [13] to be overcome.' So this was done, and they were come to his castle; but in no wise the queen would never let none of the ten knights and her ladies out of her sight, but always they were in her presence. For the book saith Sir Mellyagaunce durst make no masteries,[14] for dread of Sir Lancelot, insomuch he deemed that he had warning.

So when the child [15] was departed from the fellowship of Sir Mellyagaunce, within a while he came to Westminster, and anon he found Sir Lancelot. And when he had told his message and delivered him the queen's ring,

'Alas!' said Sir Lancelot, 'now am I shamed for ever, unless that I may rescue that noble lady from dishonour.'

Then eagerly he asked his arms. And ever [16] the child told Sir Lancelot how the ten knights fought marvellously, and how Sir Pelleas, and Sir Ironside, Sir Braundiles, and Sir Persaunt of Inde fought strongly, but namely Sir Pelleas,

[9] swiftly
[10] cunningly escaped
[11] ambush
[12] ordering

[13] too strong
[14] attacks
[15] young nobleman
[16] again

there might none harness hold [17] him; and how they all fought till they were laid to the earth, and how the queen made appointment [18] for to save their lives and to go with Sir Mellyagaunce.

'Alas,' said Sir Lancelot, 'that most noble lady, that she should be so destroyed! I had liefer,' said Sir Lancelot, 'than all France that I had been there well armed.'

So when Sir Lancelot was armed and upon his horse, he prayed the child [19] of the queen's chamber to warn Sir Lavain [20] how suddenly he was departed, and for what cause. 'And pray him as he loveth me, that he will hie him after me, and that he stint [1] not until he come to the castle where Sir Mellyagaunce abideth. For there,' said Sir Lancelot, 'he shall hear of me an I be a man living, and then shall I rescue the queen and the ten knights the which he traitorly hath taken, and that shall I prove upon his head, and all of them that hold with him.[2]

Then Sir Lancelot rode as fast as he might, and the book saith he took the water [3] at Westminster Bridge, and made his horse swim over the Thames unto Lambeth. And so within a while he came to that same place thereas [4] the ten noble knights fought with Sir Mellyagaunce. And then Sir Lancelot followed the track until that he came to a wood, and there was a strait way, and there the thirty archers bade Sir Lancelot turn again, 'and follow no longer that track.'

'What commandment have ye,' said Sir Lancelot, 'to cause me, that am a knight of the Round Table, to leave my right way?'

'These ways shalt thou leave, other else thou shalt go it on thy foot, for wit thou well thy horse shall be slain.'

'That is little mastery,' [5] said Sir Lancelot, 'to slay mine horse! But as for myself, when my horse is slain I give right nought of you, not an ye were five hundred more!'

So then they shot Sir Lancelot's horse and smote him with

---

[17] withstand
[18] contrived
[19] young nobleman
[20] *Gawain, according to* F. *Lavain, brother of Elaine, first appears in the story of* The Fair Maid of Astolat *which in* M's

collection precedes The Knight of the Cart.
[1] stop
[2] fight on his side
[3] crossed the river
[4] where
[5] no deed of prowess

many arrows. And then Sir Lancelot avoided [6] his horse and went on foot, but there were so many ditches and hedges betwixt them and him that he might not meddle with none [7] of them.

'Alas, for shame!' said Sir Lancelot, 'that ever one knight should betray another knight! But it is an old said saw, "A good man is never in danger but when he is in the danger [8] of a coward."'

Then Sir Lancelot walked on a while, and was sore acumbered of [9] his armour, his shield, and his spear. Wit you well he was full sore annoyed! And full loath he was for to leave anything that longed unto him, for he dread sore the treason of Sir Mellyagaunce.

Then by fortune there came by him a chariot [10] that came thither to fetch wood.

'Say me, carter,' said Sir Lancelot, 'what shall I give thee to suffer [11] me to leap into thy chariot, and that thou will bring me unto a castle within this two mile?'

'Thou shalt not enter this chariot,' said the carter, 'for I am sent for to fetch wood.'

'Unto whom?' said Sir Lancelot.

'Unto my lord, Sir Mellyagaunce,' said the carter.

'And with him would I speak,' said Sir Lancelot.

'Thou shalt not go with me!' said the carter.

When Sir Lancelot leapt to him and gave him backward with his gauntlet a rearmain [12] that he fell to the earth stark dead, then the other carter, his fellow, was afeard, and weened to have gone [13] the same way. And then he said,

'Fair lord, save my life, and I shall bring you where ye will.'

'Then I charge thee,' said Sir Lancelot, 'that thou drive me and this chariot unto Sir Mellyagaunce [14] gate.'

'Then leap ye up into the chariot,' said the carter, 'and ye shall be there anon.'

So the carter drove on a great wallop,[15] and Sir Lancelot's horse followed the chariot, with more than forty arrows in him.

---

[6] dismounted from
[7] could not fight with any
[8] at the mercy. *In the phrase 'never in danger' the word is used in the modern sense.*
[9] heavily burdened with
[10] cart
[11] let
[12] back-handed stroke
[13] thought he would fare
[14] Mellyagaunce's
[15] at full speed

And more than an hour and an half Queen Guinevere was awaiting in a bay window. Then one of her ladies espied an armed knight standing in a chariot.

'Ah, see, madam,' said the lady, 'where rideth in a chariot a goodly armed knight, and we suppose he rideth unto hanging.'

'Where?' said the queen.

Then she espied by his shield that it was Sir Lancelot, and then she was ware where came his horse after the chariot, and ever he trod his guts and his paunch under his feet.

'Alas,' said the queen, 'now I may prove and see that well is that creature that hath a trusty friend. A ha!' said Queen Guinevere, 'I see well that ye were hard bestead when [16] ye ride in a chariot.' And then she rebuked that lady that likened Sir Lancelot to ride in a chariot to hanging: 'Forsooth, it was foul-mouthed,' said the queen, 'and evil-likened, so for to liken the most noble knight of the world unto such a shameful death. Ah! Jesu defend him and keep him,' said the queen, 'from all mischievous [17] end!'

So by this was Sir Lancelot comen to the gates of that castle, and there he descended down and cried, that all the castle might ring:

'Where art thou, thou false traitor, Sir Mellyagaunce, and knight of the Table Round? Come forth, thou traitor knight, thou and all thy fellowship with thee, for here I am, Sir Lancelot du Lake, that shall fight with you all!'

And therewithal he bare [18] the gate wide open upon the porter, and smote him under the ear with his gauntlet, that his neck brast [19] in two pieces. When Sir Mellyagaunce heard that Sir Lancelot was comen he ran unto the queen and fell upon his knee and said:

'Mercy, madam, for now I put me wholly in your good grace.'

'What aileth you now?' said Queen Guinevere. 'Perdy,[20] I might well wit that some good knight would revenge me, though my lord King Arthur knew not of this your work.'

'Ah, madam,' said Sir Mellyagaunce, 'all this that is amiss on

[16] hard-pressed if   [19] broke
[17] shameful   [20] par Dieu
[18] forced

my party [1] shall be amended right as yourself will devise, and wholly I put me in your grace.'

'What would ye that I did?' said the queen.

'Madam, I would no more,' said Sir Mellyagaunce, 'but that ye would take all in your own hands, and that ye will rule my lord Sir Lancelot.[2] And such cheer as may be made him in this poor castle, ye and he shall have until to-morn, and then may ye and all they return again unto Westminster. And my body and all that I have I shall put in your rule.'

'Ye say well,' said the queen, 'and better is peace than evermore war, and the less noise [3] the more is my worship.'

Then the queen and her ladies went down unto Sir Lancelot that stood wood wroth [4] out of measure in the inner court to abide battle, and ever [5] he said: 'Thou traitor knight, come forth!' Then the queen came unto him and said,

'Sir Lancelot, why be ye so amoved?' [6]

'Ah, madam,' said Sir Lancelot, 'why ask ye me that question? For meseemeth ye ought to be more wrother than I am, for ye have the hurt and the dishonour. For wit you well, madam, my hurt is but little in regard for the slaying of a mare's son, but the despite [7] grieveth me much more than all my hurt.'

'Truly,' said the queen, 'ye say truth, but [8] heartily I thank you,' said the queen. 'But ye must come in with me peaceably, for all thing is put in mine hand, and all that is amiss shall be amended, for the knight full sore repenteth him of this misadventure that is befallen him.'

'Madam,' said Sir Lancelot, 'sith it is so that ye be accorded [9] with him, as for me I may not againsay it, howbeit Sir Mellyagaunce hath done full shamefully to me and cowardly. And, madam,' said Sir Lancelot, 'an I had wist ye would have been so lightly accorded [9] with him I would not a made such haste unto you.'

'Why say ye so?' said the queen. 'Do ye forthink yourself of [10] your good deeds? Wit you well,' said the queen, 'I accorded never with him for no favour nor love that I had

[1] all the wrong I have done
[2] and let my lord Sir Lancelot obey you
[3] scandal
[4] violently angry
[5] repeatedly
[6] angry
[7] insult
[8] and
[9] reconciled
[10] regret

unto him, but of every shameful noise of wisdom to lay adown.' [11]

'Madam,' said Sir Lancelot, 'ye understand full well I was never willing nor glad of shameful slander nor noise. And there is nother king, queen, ne knight that beareth the life, except my lord King Arthur, and you, madam, that should let [12] me but I should make Sir Mellyagaunce [13] heart full cold or ever I departed from hence.'

'That wot I well,' said the queen, 'but what will ye more? Ye shall have all thing ruled as ye list to have it.'

'Madam,' said Sir Lancelot, 'so [14] ye be pleased, as for my part ye shall soon please me.'

Right so the queen took Sir Lancelot by the bare hand, for he had put off his gauntlet, and so she went with him till her chamber; and then she commanded him to be unarmed.

And then Sir Lancelot asked the queen where were her ten knights that were wounded with her. Then she showed them unto him, and there they made great joy of the coming of Sir Lancelot, and he made great sorrow of their hurts. And there Sir Lancelot told them how cowardly and traitorly he [15] set archers to slay his horse, and how he was fain to put himself in a chariot. And thus they complained everych to other, and full fain they would have been revenged, but they kept the peace because of the queen.

Then, as the French book saith, Sir Lancelot was called many days after 'le Chevalier de Chariot,' and so he did many deeds and great adventures.

AND SO WE LEAVE OFF HERE OF LE CHEVALIER DE CHARIOT, AND TURN WE TO THIS TALE.

So Sir Lancelot had great cheer with the queen. And then he made a promise with the queen that the same night he should come to a window outward toward a garden, and that window was barred with iron, and there Sir Lancelot promised to meet her when all folks were on sleep.

So then came Sir Lavain driving to the gates, saying, 'Where is my lord, Sir Lancelot?' Anon he was sent for, and when Sir Lavain saw Sir Lancelot, he said,

---

[11] wisely to prevent any scandal
[12] prevent
[13] Mellyagaunce's
[14] if it pleases you
[15] = Mellyagaunce

'Ah, my lord, I found how ye were hard bestead,[16] for I have found your horse that was slain with arrows.'

'As for that,' said Sir Lancelot, 'I pray you, Sir Lavain, speak ye of other matters and let this pass, and right it another time an we may.'

Then the knights that were hurt were searched,[17] and soft salves were laid to their wounds, and so it passed on till supper time. And all the cheer that might be made them there was done unto the queen and all her knights. And when season was [18] they went unto their chambers, but in no wise the queen would not suffer her wounded knights to be from her, but that they were laid inwith draughts by [19] her chamber, upon beds and pallets, that she herself might see unto them that they wanted nothing.

So when Sir Lancelot was in his chamber which was assigned unto him, he called unto him Sir Lavain, and told him that night he must speak with his lady, Queen Guinevere.

'Sir,' said Sir Lavain, 'let me go with you an it please you, for I dread me sore of the treason of Sir Mellyagaunce.'

'Nay,' said Sir Lancelot, 'I thank you, but I will have nobody with me.'

Then Sir Lancelot took his sword in his hand and privily went to the place where he had spied a ladder toforehand, and that he took under his arm, and bare it through the garden and set it up to the window. And anon the queen was there ready to meet him.

And then they made their complaints to other of many divers things, and then Sir Lancelot wished that he might have comen in to her.

'Wit you well,' said the queen, 'I would as fain as ye that ye might come in to me.'

'Would ye so, madam,' said Sir Lancelot, 'with your heart that I were with you?'

'Yea, truly,' said the queen.

'Then shall I prove my might,' said Sir Lancelot, 'for your love.'

And then he set his hands upon the bars of iron and pulled at them with such a might that he brast [20] them clean out of

---

[16] hard-pressed
[17] had their wounds probed
[18] at the proper time

[19] in the recesses of
[20] tore

the stone walls. And therewithal one of the bars of iron cut the brawn [1] of his hands thoroughout to the bone. And then he leapt into the chamber to the queen.

'Make ye no noise,' said the queen, 'for my wounded knights lie here fast by me.'

So, to pass upon [2] this tale, Sir Lancelot went to bed with the queen, and took no force [3] of his hurt hand, but took his pleasaunce and his liking [4] until it was the dawning of the day; for wit you well he slept not, but watched.[5] And when he saw his time that he might tarry no longer, he took his leave and departed at the window, and put it together as well as he might again, and so departed until his own chamber. And there he told Sir Lavain how he was hurt. Then Sir Lavain dressed his hand and staunched it, and put upon it a glove, that it should not be espied. And so they lay long abed in the morning till it was nine of the clock.

Then Sir Mellyagaunce went to the queen's chamber and found her ladies there ready clothed.

'Ah, Jesu mercy,' said Sir Mellyagaunce, 'what ails you, madam, that ye sleep this long?'

And therewithal he opened the curtain for to behold her. And then was he ware where she lay, and all the head-sheet, pillow and over-sheet was bebled of the blood [6] of Sir Lancelot and of his hurt hand. When Sir Mellyagaunce espied that blood then he deemed in her that she was [7] false to the king, and that some of the wounded knights had lain by her all that night.

'A ha, madam,' said Sir Mellyagaunce, 'now I have found you a false traitress unto my lord Arthur, for now I prove well [8] it was not for nought that ye laid these wounded knights within the bounds of your chamber. Therefore I call you [9] of treason before my lord King Arthur. And now I have proved you, madam, with [10] a shameful deed; and that they been all false, or some of them, I will make it good,[11] for a wounded knight this night hath lain by you.'

---

[1] flesh
[2] continue briefly with
[3] took no notice
[4] his pleasure and his joy
[5] lay awake
[6] covered with the blood
[7] suspected her of being
[8] declare
[9] accuse you
[10] found you guilty, madam, of
[11] prove it

'That is false,' said the queen, 'that I will report me unto them.' [12]

But [13] when the ten knights heard of Sir Mellyagaunce's words, and then they spake all at once, and said,

'Sir Mellyagaunce, thou falsely beliest [14] my lady the queen, and that we will make good [15] upon thee, any of us. Now choose which thou list of us, when we are whole of the wounds thou gavest us.'

'Ye shall not! Away with your proud language! For here ye may all see that a wounded knight this night hath lain by the queen.'

Then they all looked and were sore ashamed [16] when they saw that blood. And wit you well Sir Mellyagaunce was passing glad that he had the queen at such advantage, for he deemed by that to hide his own treason.

And so in this rumour [17] came in Sir Lancelot and found them at a great affray.[18]

'What array is this?' [19] said Sir Lancelot.

Then Sir Mellyagaunce told them what he had found, and so he showed him the queen's bed.

'Now, truly,' said Sir Lancelot, 'ye did not your part nor knightly, to touch a queen's bed while it was drawn [20] and she lying therein. And I dare say,' said Sir Lancelot, 'my lord King Arthur himself would not have displayed [1] her curtains, and she being within her bed, unless that it had pleased him to have lain him down by her. And therefore, Sir Mellyagaunce, ye have done unworshipfully and shamefully to yourself.'

'Sir, I wot not what ye mean,' said Sir Mellyagaunce, 'but well I am sure there hath one of her hurt knights lain with her this night. And that will I prove with mine hands, that she is a traitress unto my lord King Arthur.'

'Beware what ye do,' said Sir Lancelot, 'for an ye say so, and will prove it, it will be taken at your hands.' [2]

---

[12] I shall ask them to bear witness

[13] And

[14] slanderest

[15] prove

[16] perturbed

[17] as they were arguing

[18] greatly disturbed

[19] what is the matter?

[20] while the curtains were drawn

[1] opened

[2] your challenge will be accepted

'My lord Sir Lancelot,' said Sir Mellyagaunce, 'I read [3] you beware what ye do; for though ye are never so good a knight, as I wot well ye are renowned the best knight of the world, yet should ye be advised to do [4] battle in a wrong quarrel, for God will have a stroke in every battle.'

'As for that,' said Sir Lancelot, 'God is to be dread! But as to that, I say nay plainly, that this night there lay none of these ten knights wounded with my lady Queen Guinevere, and that will I prove with mine hands that ye say untruly in that. Now, what say ye?' said Sir Lancelot.

'Thus I say,' said Sir Mellyagaunce, 'here is my glove, that she is a traitress unto my lord King Arthur, and that this night one of the wounded knights lay with her.'

'Well, sir, and I receive your glove,' said Sir Lancelot.

And anon they were sealed [5] with their signets, and delivered unto the ten knights.

'At what day shall we do battle together?' said Sir Lancelot.

'This day eight days,' said Sir Mellyagaunce, 'in the field beside Westminster.'

'I am agreed,' said Sir Lancelot.

'But now,' said Sir Mellyagaunce, 'sithen it is so that we must needs fight together, I pray you, as ye be a noble knight, await me with no treason [6] nother no villainy the meanwhile, nother none for you.' [7]

'So God me help,' said Sir Lancelot, 'ye shall right well wit I was never of no such conditions.[8] For I report me to all knights that ever have known me,[9] I fared never with no treason, nother I loved never the fellowship of him that fared with treason.'

'Then let us go unto dinner,' said Sir Mellyagaunce, 'and after dinner the queen and ye may ride all unto Westminster.'

'I will well,' said Sir Lancelot.

Then Sir Mellyagaunce said to Sir Lancelot,

'Sir, pleaseth you to see estures [10] of this castle?'

'With a good will,' said Sir Lancelot.

---

[3] advise
[4] you should beware of doing
[5] their challenge was sealed
[6] do not try to betray me
[7] and none shall be done to you

[8] I have never been guilty of such a behaviour
[9] I call upon all those knights who have ever known me to confirm that
[10] rooms

And then they went together from chamber to chamber, for Sir Lancelot dread no perils; for ever a man of worship and of prowess dreads but little of perils, for they ween that every man be as they been. But ever he that fareth with treason putteth often a true man in great danger. And so it befell upon Sir Lancelot that no peril dread: as he went with Sir Mellyagaunce he trod on a trap, and the board rolled, and there Sir Lancelot fell down more than ten fathom into a cave full of straw.

And then Sir Mellyagaunce departed and made no fare,[11] no more than he that wist not where he [12] was. And when Sir Lancelot was thus missed they marvelled where he was becomen,[13] and then the queen and many of them deemed that he was departed, as he was wont to do, suddenly. For Sir Mellyagaunce made suddenly to put on side Sir Lavain's horse, that they might all understand that Sir Lancelot were departed suddenly.

So then it passed on till after dinner, and then Sir Lavain would not stint until he had horse-litters for the wounded knights, that they might be carried in them. And so with the queen both ladies and gentlewomen and other rode unto Westminister, and there the knights told how Sir Mellyagaunce had appealed [14] the queen of high treason, and how Sir Lancelot received the glove of him: 'And this day eight days they shall do battle before you.'

'By my head,' said King Arthur, 'I am afeard Sir Mellyagaunce hath charged himself with a great charge.[15] But where is Sir Lancelot?' said the king.

'Sir, we wot not where he is, but we deem he is ridden to some adventure, as he is oftentimes wont to do, for he hath Sir Lavain's horse.'

'Let him be,' said the king, 'for he will be founden but if he be trapped with some treason.'

Thus leave we Sir Lancelot lying within that cave in great pain.[16] And every day there came a lady and brought his meat and his drink, and wooed him every day to have lain

---

[11] went away quietly
[12] as if he did not know where Lancelot was
[13] what had become of him

[14] accused
[15] taken upon himself a heavy task
[16] distress

by her; and ever Sir Lancelot said her nay. Then said she:

'Sir, ye are not wise, for ye may never out of this prison but if ye have my help. And also your lady, Queen Guinevere, shall be brent in your default [17] unless that ye be there at the day of battle.'

'God defend,' said Sir Lancelot, 'that she should be brent in my default! And if it be so,' said Sir Lancelot, 'that I may not be there, it shall be well understood, both at [18] the king and the queen and with [18] all men of worship, that I am dead-sick other [19] in prison. For all men that know me will say for me that I am in some evil case [20] an I be not that day there. And thus well I understand that there is some good knight, other of my blood other some other that loves me, that will take my quarrel in hand. And therefore,' said Sir Lancelot, 'wit you well, ye shall not fear [1] me, and if there were no more women in all this land but ye, yet shall not I have ado with you.'

'Then are ye shamed,' said the lady, 'and destroyed for ever.'

'As for world's shame, now Jesu defend me! And as for my distress, it is welcome, whatsomever it be that God sends me.'

So she came to him again the same day that the battle should be and said,

'Sir Lancelot, bethink you, for ye are too hard-hearted. And therefore an ye would but once kiss me I should deliver you and your armour, and the best horse that was within Sir Mellyagaunce [2] stable.'

'As for to kiss you,' said Sir Lancelot, 'I may do that and lose no worship. And wit you well an I understood there were any disworship for to kiss you, I would not do it.'

And then he kissed her, and anon she gat him up until [3] his armour. And when he was armed she brought him till [3] a stable where stood twelve good coursers, and bade him to choose the best. Then Sir Lancelot looked upon a white courser and that liked him best, and anon he commanded him to be

[17] burnt through your failure to appear
[18] by
[19] gravely ill or
[20] plight
[1] frighten
[2] Mellyagaunce's
[3] brought him to

saddled with the best saddle of war, and so it was done. Then he gat his own spear in his hand and his sword by his side, and then he commended the lady unto God, and said,

'Lady, for this day's deed I shall do you service if ever it lie in my power.'

Now leave we here Sir Lancelot, all that ever he might wallop,[4] and speak we of Queen Guinevere that was brought till a fire to be brent; for Sir Mellyagaunce was sure, him thought, that Sir Lancelot should not be at that battle, and therefore he ever cried upon Sir Arthur to do [5] him justice other else bring forth Sir Lancelot. Then was the king and all the court full sore abashed and shamed that the queen should have be brent in the default of Sir Lancelot.[6]

'My lord, King Arthur,' said Sir Lavain, 'ye may understand that it is not well with my lord Sir Lancelot, for an he were on live, so he be not sick other in prison, wit you well he would have been here. For never heard ye that ever he failed yet his part for whom he should do battle for. And therefore,' said Sir Lavain, 'my lord, King Arthur, I beseech you that ye will give me license to do battle here this day for my lord and master, and for to save my lady the queen.'

'Gramercy, gentle Sir Lavain,' said King Arthur, 'for I dare say all that Sir Mellyagaunce putteth upon my lady the queen is wrong. For I have spoken with all the ten wounded knights, and there is not one of them, an he were whole and able to do battle, but he would prove upon Sir Mellyagaunce [7] body that it is false that he putteth upon my lady.'

'And so shall I,' said Sir Lavain, 'in the defence of my lord, Sir Lancelot, an ye will give me leave.'

'And I give you leave,' said King Arthur, 'and do your best, for I dare well say there is some treason done to Sir Lancelot.'

Then was Sir Lavain armed and horsed, and deliverly [8] at the lists' end he rode to perform his battle. And right as the heralds should cry: *Laissez-les aller!* [9] right so came Sir Lancelot driving with all the might of his horse. And then King Arthur cried 'Wo!' and 'Abide!'

---

4 gallop
5 kept calling upon Sir Arthur to give
6 because of Sir Lancelot's failure to take up the challenge
7 Mellyagaunce's
8 quickly
9 let them go

And then Sir Lancelot called [10] tofore King Arthur, and there he told openly tofore the king all how that Sir Mellyagaunce had served him first and last. And when the king and queen and all the lords knew of the treason of Sir Mellyagaunce, they were all ashamed on his behalf. Then was the queen sent for and set by the king in the great trust of her champion.

And then Sir Lancelot and Sir Mellyagaunce dressed them together [11] with spears as thunder, and there Sir Lancelot bare him quit [12] over his horse's croup.[13] And then Sir Lancelot alight and dressed his shield on his shoulder, and took his sword in his hand, and so they dressed to each other [11] and smote many great strokes together. And at the last Sir Lancelot smote him such a buffet upon the helmet that he fell on the one side to the earth. And then he cried upon him [14] loud and said,

'Most noble knight, Sir Lancelot, save my life! For I yield me unto you, and I require you, as ye be a knight and fellow of the Table Round, slee me not, for I yield me as overcomen; and whether I shall live or die I put me in the king's hand and yours.'

Then Sir Lancelot wist not what to do, for he had liefer than all the good in the world he might be revenged upon him. So Sir Lancelot looked upon the queen, if he might espy by any sign or countenance what she would have done. And anon the queen wagged her head upon [15] Sir Lancelot, as who saith,[16] 'Slay him!' And full well knew Sir Lancelot by her signs that she would have him dead. Then Sir Lancelot bade him,

'Arise for shame, and perform this battle with me to the utterance.'

'Nay,' said Sir Mellyagaunce, 'I will never arise until that ye take me as yolden and recreant.' [17]

'Well, I shall proffer you a large proffer,' [18] said Sir Lancelot, 'that is for to say I shall unarm my head and my left quarter of my body, all that may be unarmed as for that

[10] brought a charge
[11] came together
[12] threw him off
[13] hind-quarters
[14] begged him
[15] nodded to

[16] as if to say (*Old Fr.: comme celle qui dit*)
[17] as one who has yielded and surrendered
[18] make you a generous offer

quarter, and I will let bind my left hand behind me there [19] it shall not help me, and right so I shall do battle with you.'

Then Sir Mellyagaunce start up and said on hight,

'Take heed, my lord Arthur, of this proffer,[20] for I will take it. And let him be disarmed and bounden according to his proffer.'

'What say ye?' said King Arthur unto Sir Lancelot. 'Will ye abide by your proffer?'

'Yea, my lord,' said Sir Lancelot, 'for I will never go from that I have once said.'

Then the knights parters of the field [1] disarmed Sir Lancelot, first his head and then his left arm and his left side, and they bound his left arm to his left side fast behind his back, without shield or anything. And anon they yode together.

Wit you well there was many a lady and many a knight marvelled of Sir Lancelot that would jeopardy himself in such wise.

Then Sir Mellyagaunce came with sword all on hight,[2] and Sir Lancelot showed him openly his bare head and the bare left side. And when he weened to have smitten him upon the bare head, then lightly [3] he devoided [4] the left leg and the left side, and put his hand and his sword to [5] that stroke, and so put it on side with great sleight.[6] And then with great force Sir Lancelot smote him on the helmet such a buffet that the stroke carved the head in two parties.[7]

Then there was no more to do, but he was drawn out of the field, and at the great instance of the knights of the Table Round the king suffered him to be interred, and the mention made upon him who slew him and for what cause he was slain.

And then the king and the queen made more of Sir Lancelot, and more he was cherished than ever he was aforehand.

. . . And so I leave here of this tale and overleap great books of Sir Lancelot, what great adventures he did when he was

---

[19] where
[20] offer
[1] stewards
[2] holding his sword high
[3] quickly

[4] withdrew
[5] against
[6] skill
[7] halves

called Le Chevalier de Chariot. For, as the French book saith, because of despite that knights and ladies [8] called him 'the knight that rode in the chariot,' like as [9] he were judged to the gibbet, therefore, in the despite of all them that [10] named him so, he was carried in a chariot a twelvemonth; for but little after that [11] he had slain Sir Mellyagaunce in the queen's quarrel he never of a twelvemonth come on horseback. And as the French book saith, he did that twelvemonth more than forty battles.

[8] because he had been insulted by knights and ladies who

[9] as if

[10] out of contempt for all those who

[11] soon after

Lancelot and Elaine

As the book of French maketh mention, afore the time that
Sir Galahad was begotten or born, there came in an hermit
unto King Arthur upon Whitsunday, as the knights sat at
the Table Round. And when the hermit saw the Siege Perilous he asked the king and all the knights why that siege was
void.

Then King Arthur for all the knights answered and said,
'There shall never none sit in that siege but one, but if he
be destroyed.'

Then said the hermit, 'Sir, wot ye what he is?'

'Nay,' said King Arthur and all the knights, 'we know not
who he is yet that shall sit there.'

'Then wot I,' said the hermit. 'For he that shall sit there
is yet unborn and unbegotten, and this same year he shall be
begotten that shall sit in that Siege Perilous, and he shall win
the Sankgreall.' When this hermit had made this mention he
departed from the court of King Arthur.

And so after this feast Sir Lancelot rode on his adventure
till on a time by adventure he passed over the Pont de
Corbin. And there he saw the fairest tower that ever he saw,
and thereunder was a fair little town full of people. And all
the people, men and women, cried at once.

'Welcome, Sir Lancelot, the flower of knighthood! For by
thee all we shall be holpen out of danger.' [1]

'What mean ye,' said Sir Lancelot, 'that ye cry thus upon
me?'

'Ah, fair knight,' said they all, 'here is within this tower a
dolorous [2] lady that hath been there in pains many winters

---

[1] delivered   [2] unfortunate

and days, for ever she boileth in scalding water. And but late,' said all the people, 'Sir Gawain was here and he might not help her, and so he left her in pain still.'[3]

'Peradventure [4] so may I,' said Sir Lancelot, 'leave her in pain as well as Sir Gawain.'

'Nay,' said the people, 'we know well that it is ye, Sir Lancelot, that shall deliver her.'

'Well,' said Sir Lancelot, 'then tell me what I shall [5] do.'

And so anon they brought Sir Lancelot into the tower. And when he came to the chamber thereas [6] this lady was, the doors of iron unlocked and unbolted, and so Sir Lancelot went into the chamber that was as hot as any stew.[7] And there Sir Lancelot took the fairest lady by the hand that ever he saw, and she was as naked as a needle. And by enchantment Queen Morgan le Fay and the Queen of North Wales had put her there in that pains, because she was called the fairest lady of that country; and there she had been five year, and never might she be delivered out of her pains unto the time the best knight of the world had taken her by the hand.

Then the people brought her clothes, and when she was arrayed Sir Lancelot thought she was the fairest lady that ever he saw but if it were Queen Guinevere. Then this lady said to Sir Lancelot,

'Sir, if it please you, will ye go with me hereby into a chapel, that we may give loving [8] to God?'

'Madam,' said Sir Lancelot, 'cometh on with me and I will go with you.'

So when they came there they gave thankings to God, all the people both learned and lewd,[9] and said,

'Sir knight, syn ye have delivered this lady ye must deliver us also from a serpent which is here in a tomb.'

Then Sir Lancelot took his shield and said,

'Sirs, bring me thither, and what that I may do to the pleasure of God and of you I shall do.'

---

3 where she was
4 perhaps
5 must
6 where

7 stove
8 praise
9 ignorant

So when Sir Lancelot come thither he saw written upon
the tomb with letters of gold that said thus:

'HERE SHALL COME A LEOPARD OF KING'S BLOOD AND HE SHALL
SLAY THIS SERPENT. AND THIS LEOPARD SHALL ENGENDER A LION
IN THIS FOREIGN COUNTRY WHICH LION SHALL PASS ALL OTHER
KNIGHTS.'

So when Sir Lancelot had lift up the tomb there came out
an horrible and a fiendly dragon spitting wild fire out of his
mouth. Then Sir Lancelot drew his sword and fought with
that dragon long, and at the last with great pain Sir Lancelot
slew that dragon.

And therewithal come King Pelles, the good and noble
king, and salewed Sir Lancelot and he him again.

'Now, fair knight,' said the king, 'what is your name? I
require you of your knighthood tell ye me.'

'Sir,' said Sir Lancelot, 'wit you well my name is Sir
Lancelot du Lake.'

'And my name is King Pelles, king of the foreign country
and cousin nigh unto Joseph of Arimathea.'

And then either of them made much of other, and so they
went into the castle to take their repast. And anon there
came in a dove at a window, and in her mouth there seemed
a little censer of gold, and therewithal there was such a savour [10] as all the spicery [11] of the world had been there. And
forthwithal there was upon the table all manner of meats and
drinks that they could think upon.

So there came in a damsel passing fair and young, and she
bare a vessel of gold betwixt her hands; and thereto the king
kneeled devoutly and said his prayers, and so did all that were
there.

'Ah, Jesu,' said Sir Lancelot, 'what may this mean?'

'Sir,' said the king, 'this is the richest thing that any man
hath living, and when this thing goeth abroad the Round
Table shall be broken for a season.[12] And wit you well,' said
the king, 'this is the Holy Sankgreall that ye have here
seen.'

So the king and Sir Lancelot led their life the most party

[10] scent
[11] spices

[12] for a time

of that day [13] together. And fain would King Pelles have found
the mean that [14] Sir Lancelot should have lain by his daughter,
fair Elaine, and for this intent: the king knew well that Sir
Lancelot should get a pusell [15] upon his daughter, which
should be called Sir Galahad, the good knight by whom all
the foreign country should be brought out of danger;[16] and
by him the Holy Grail should be achieved.

Then came forth a lady that hight Dame Brusen, and she
said unto the king,

'Sir, wit you well Sir Lancelot loveth no lady in the world
but all only [17] Queen Guinevere. And therefore work ye by
my counsel, and I shall make him to lie with your daughter,
and he shall not wit [18] but that he lieth by Queen Guinevere.'

'Ah, fair lady,' said the king, 'hope ye that ye may bring
this matter about?'

'Sir,' said she, 'upon pain of my life, let me deal.'

For this Dame Brusen was one of the greatest enchanters
that was that time in the world.

And so anon by Dame Brusen's wit she made one to come
to Sir Lancelot that he knew well, and this man brought a
ring from Queen Guinevere like as it had come from her, and
such one as she was wont for the most part to wear. And when
Sir Lancelot saw that token, wit you well he was never so fain.

'Where is my lady?' said Sir Lancelot.

'In the castle of Case,' said the messenger, 'but five mile
hence.'

Then thought Sir Lancelot to be there the same night.
And then this Dame Brusen, by the commandment of King
Pelles, she let send Elaine to this castle with five-and-twenty
knights, unto the castle of Case.

Then Sir Lancelot against [19] night rode unto the castle, and
there anon he was received worshipfully with such people,
to his seeming,[20] as were about Queen Guinevere secret.[1]
So when Sir Lancelot was alight he asked where the queen
was. So Dame Brusen said she was in her bed.

---

[13] that day spent most of their
time
[14] how to contrive that
[15] chaste youth
[16] delivered
[17] except

[18] so that he shall not think otherwise
[19] shortly before
[20] as it seemed to him
[1] in Queen Guinevere's
confidence

And then people were avoided,[2] and Sir Lancelot was led into her chamber. And then Dame Brusen brought Sir Lancelot a cup of wine, and anon as he had drunken that wine he was so assotted[3] and mad that he might make no delay, but without any let[4] he went to bed. And so he weened that maiden Elaine had been Queen Guinevere. And wit you well that Sir Lancelot was glad, and so was lady Elaine that she had gotten Sir Lancelot in her arms, for well she knew that that same night should be begotten Sir Galahad upon her, that should prove the best knight of the world.

And so they lay together until undern of the morn;[5] and all the windows and holes[6] of that chamber were stopped, that no manner of day[7] might be seen. And anon Sir Lancelot remembered him and arose up and went to the window, and anon as he had unshut the window the enchantment was past. Then he knew himself that he had done amiss.

'Alas!' he said, 'that I have lived so long, for now am I shamed.'

And anon he gat his sword in his hand and said,

'Thou traitress! What art thou that I have lain by all this night? Thou shalt die right here of[8] mine hands!'

Then this fair lady Elaine skipped out of her bed all naked and said,

'Fair courteous knight, Sir Lancelot,' kneeling before him, 'ye are come of king's blood, and therefore I require you have mercy upon me! And as thou art renowned the most noble knight of the world, slay me not, for I have in my womb begotten of thee that shall be the most noblest knight of the world.'

'Ah, false traitress! Why hast thou betrayed me? Tell me, anon,' said Sir Lancelot, 'what thou art.'

'Sir,' she said, 'I am Elaine, the daughter of King Pelles.'

'Well,' said Sir Lancelot, 'I will forgive you.'

And therewith he took her up in his arms and kissed her, for she was a fair lady, and thereto lusty and young, and wise as any was that time living.

---

[2] sent away
[3] infatuated
[4] unhindered
[5] nine o'clock the next morning
[6] embrasures
[7] daylight
[8] by

'So God me help,' said Sir Lancelot, 'I may not wite this to you,[9] but her that made this enchantment upon me and between you and me. An I may find her, that same lady Dame Brusen shall lose her head for her witchcrafts, for there was never knight deceived as I am this night.'

And then she said, 'My lord, Sir Lancelot, I beseech you, see me as soon as ye may, for I have obeyed me unto the prophecy that my father told me. And by his commandment, to fulfil this prophecy I have given thee the greatest riches and the fairest flower that ever I had, and that is my maidenhood that I shall never have again. And therefore, gentle knight, owe me your goodwill.'

And so Sir Lancelot arrayed him and armed him, and took his leave mildly at [10] that young lady Elaine. And so he departed and rode to the castle of Corbin where her father was.

And as fast as her time came she was delivered of a fair child, and they christened him Galahad. And wit you well that child was well kept and well nourished, and he was so named Galahad because Sir Lancelot was so named at the fountain stone (and after that the Lady of the Lake confirmed him Sir Lancelot du Lake).

Then after the lady was delivered and churched there came a knight unto her, his name was Sir Bromell la Pleche, the which was a great lord. And he had loved that lady Elaine long, and he evermore desired to wed her. And so by no mean she could put him off, till on a day she said to Sir Bromell,

'Wit you well, sir knight, I will not love you, for my love is set upon the best knight of the world.'

'Who is that?' said Sir Bromell.

'Sir,' she said, 'it is Sir Lancelot du Lake that I love and none other, and therefore woo ye me no longer.'

'Ye say well,' said Sir Bromell, 'and sithen ye have told me so much, ye shall have little joy of Sir Lancelot, for I shall slee him wheresomever I meet him!'

'Sir,' said this lady Elaine, 'do to him no treason, and God forbid that ye spare [11] him.'

'Well, my lady,' said Sir Bromell, 'and I shall promise you

---

[9] blame you for this   [11] find
[10] gently bade farewell to

this twelvemonth and a day I shall keep Le Pont Corbin for Sir Lancelot sake, that he shall nother come nother go unto you, but I shall meet with him.'

Then as it fell by fortune and adventure, Sir Bors de Ganis that was nephew unto Sir Lancelot came over that bridge; and there Sir Bromell and Sir Bors jousted, and Sir Bors smote Sir Bromell such a buffet that he bare him over his horse croup.[12]

And then Sir Bromell, as an hardy [13] man, pulled out his sword and dressed his shield to do battle with Sir Bors. And anon Sir Bors alight and voided [14] his horse, and there they dashed together [15] many sad strokes. And long thus they fought, and at the last Sir Bromell was laid to the earth, and there Sir Bors began to unlace his helm to slee him. Then Sir Bromell cried him mercy and yielded him.

'Upon this covenant thou shalt have thy life,' said Sir Bors, 'so thou go unto my lord Sir Lancelot upon Whitsunday next coming and yield thee unto him as a knight recreant.' [16]

'Sir, I will do it,' said Sir Bromell.

And so he sware upon the cross of the sword, and so he [17] let him depart. And Sir Bors rode unto King Pelles, that was within Corbin, and when the king and Elaine, his daughter, knew that Sir Bors was nephew unto Sir Lancelot they made him great cheer. Then said Dame Elaine,

'We marvel where Sir Lancelot is, for he came never here but once that ever I saw.'

'Madam, marvel ye not,' said Sir Bors, 'for this half year he hath been in prison with Queen Morgan le Fay, King Arthur's sister.'

'Alas!' said Dame Elaine, 'that me sore repenteth!'

And ever Sir Bors beheld that child in her arms, and ever him seemed it was passing like Sir Lancelot.

'Truly,' said Dame Elaine, 'wit you well, this child he begat upon me.'

Then Sir Bors wept for joy, and there he prayed to God it might prove as good a knight as his father was.

[12] horse's hind-quarters
[13] brave
[14] left
[15] fell upon each other with
[16] as a knight who has surrendered
[17] = Bors

And so there came in a white dove, and she bare a little censer of gold in her mouth, and there was all manner of meats and drinks. And a maiden bare that Sankgreall, and she said there openly,

'Wit you well, Sir Bors, that this child, Sir Galahad, shall sit in the Siege Perilous and achieve the Sankgreall, and he shall be much better than ever was his father, Sir Lancelot, that is his own father.'

And then they kneeled down and made their devotions, and there was such a savour [18] as all the spicery [19] in the world had been there. And as the dove had taken her flight the maiden vanished with the Sankgreall as she came.

'Sir,' said Sir Bors then unto King Pelles, 'this castle may be named the Castle Adventurous, for here be many strange adventures.'

'That is sooth,' said the king, 'for well may this place be called the adventurous place. For there come but few knights here that goeth away with any worship;[20] be he never [1] so strong, here he may be proved.[2] And but late ago Sir Gawain, the good knight, gat little worship [3] here. For I let you wit,' said King Pelles, 'here shall no knight win worship [3] but if he be of worship [4] himself and of good living,[5] and that loveth God and dreadeth God. And else he getteth no worship [20] here, be he never [1] so hardy [6] a man.'

'That is a wonder thing,' said Sir Bors, 'what ye mean in [7] this country, for ye have many strange adventures. And therefore will I lie in this castle this night.'

'Sir, ye shall not do so,' said King Pelles, 'by my counsel, for it is hard an ye escape without a shame.' [8]

'Sir, I shall take the adventure that will fall,' [9] said Sir Bors.

'Then I counsel you,' said the king, 'to be clean confessed.'

'As for that,' said Sir Bors, 'I will be shriven with a good will.'

So Sir Bors was confessed. And for all women Sir Bors

---

[18] scent
[19] spices
[20] credit
[1] ever
[2] put to the test
[3] distinction
[4] honourable

[5] righteous
[6] brave
[7] what you say about
[8] for you will not easily avoid being put to shame
[9] befall

was a virgin save for one, that was the daughter of King Braundegoris, and on her he gat a child which hight Elaine. And save for her Sir Bors was a clean maiden.[10]

And so Sir Bors was led unto bed in a fair large chamber, and many doors were shut about [11] the chamber. When Sir Bors espied all those doors he avoided all the people,[12] for he might have [13] nobody with him. But in no wise Sir Bors would unarm him, but so he laid him down upon the bed.

And right so he saw a light come, that he might [14] well see a spear great and long that came straight upon him pointeling,[15] and Sir Bors seemed [16] that the head of the spear brent like a taper. And anon, or Sir Bors wist, the spear smote him in the shoulder an handbreadth in deepness, and that wound grieved Sir Bors passing sore, and then he laid him down for pain.

And anon therewithal came a knight armed with his shield on his shoulder and his sword in his hand, and he bade Sir Bors,

'Arise, sir knight, and fight with me.'

'I am sore hurt, but yet I shall not fail thee.'

And then Sir Bors start up [17] and dressed his shield, and then they lashed together mightily a great while; and at the last Sir Bors bare [18] him backward till that he came to a chamber door, and there that knight yode [19] into that chamber and rested him a great while. And when he had reposed him he came out fiercely again and began new battle with Sir Bors mightily and strongly. Then Sir Bors thought he [20] should no more go into that chamber to rest him, and so Sir Bors dressed him [1] betwixt the knight and the chamber door. And there Sir Bors smote him down, and then that knight yielded him.

'What is your name?' said Sir Bors.

'Sir, my name is Sir Bedivere of the Strait Marches.'

So Sir Bors made him to swear at Whitsunday next coming

---

[10] chaste man
[11] around
[12] made everybody withdraw
[13] wanted
[14] could
[15] point foremost
[16] it seemed to Sir Bors
[17] stood up
[18] forced
[19] stepped
[20] = the knight
[1] stepped forward

to come to the court of King Arthur, 'and yield you there as prisoner and as an overcome knight by the hands of Sir Bors.'

So thus departed Sir Bedivere of the Strait Marches. And then Sir Bors laid him down to rest. And anon he heard much noise in that chamber, and then Sir Bors espied that there came in, he wist not whether at doors or at windows, shot [2] of arrows and of quarrels [3] so thick that he marvelled, and many fell upon him and hurt him in the bare places.

And then Sir Bors was ware where came in an hideous lion. So Sir Bors dressed him to [4] that lion, and anon the lion bereft him his shield, and with his sword Sir Bors smote off the lion's head.

Right so forthwithal he saw a dragon in the court, passing perilous [5] and horrible, and there seemed to him that there were letters of gold written in his forehead, and Sir Bors thought that the letters made a signification of 'King Arthur.' And right so there came an horrible leopard and an old, and there they fought long and did great battle together. And at the last the dragon spit out of his mouth as it had been [6] an hundred dragons; and lightly all the small dragons slew the old dragon and tore him all to pieces.

And anon and forthwithal there came an old man into the hall, and he sat him down in a fair chair, and there seemed to be two adders about his neck. And then the old man had an harp, and there he sang an old lay of Joseph of Arimathea how he came into this land. And when he had sungen, this old man bade Sir Bors go from thence. 'For here shall ye have no more adventures; yet full worshipfully have ye achieved this, and better shall ye do hereafter.'

And then Sir Bors seemed that there came the whitest dove that ever he saw with a little golden censer in her mouth. And anon therewithal the tempest ceased and passed away that afore was marvellous to hear.[7] So was all that court full of good savours.[8]

Then Sir Bors saw four fair children bearing four fair tapers, and an old man in the midst of these children with a

---

[2] a flight
[3] arrowheads, short arrows
[4] advanced towards
[5] frightening

[6] what looked like
[7] made such noise
[8] scents

censer in his hand, and a spear in his other hand, and that spear was called the Spear of Vengeance.

'Now,' said that old man to Sir Bors, 'go ye to your cousin Sir Lancelot and tell him this adventure had been most convenient [9] for him of all earthly knights, but sin is so foul in him that he may not achieve none such holy deeds; for had not been his sin, he had passed all the knights that ever were in his days. And tell thou Sir Lancelot, of [10] all worldly adventures he passeth in manhood and prowess all other, but in these spiritual matters he shall have many his better.'

And then Sir Bors saw four gentlewomen come by him, poorly beseen: [11] and he saw where that they entered into a chamber where [12] was great light as it were a summer's light. And the women kneeled down before an altar of silver with four pillars, as it had been a bishop which kneeled afore the table of silver. And as Sir Bors looked over his head he saw a sword like silver, naked, hoving [13] over his head, and clearness thereof smote in [14] his eyen, that as at that time [15] Sir Bors was blind.

And there he heard a voice which said, 'Go hence, thou Sir Bors, for as yet thou art not worthy for to be in this place!' And then he yode backward till [16] his bed till on the morn.

And so on the morn King Pelles made great joy of Sir Bors, and then he departed and rode unto Camelot. And there he found Sir Lancelot, and told him of the adventures that he had seen with King Pelles at Corbin.

And so the noise sprang in King Arthur's court that Sir Lancelot had gotten a child upon Elaine, the daughter of King Pelles, wherefore Queen Guinevere was wroth, and she gave many rebukes to Sir Lancelot and called him false knight. And then Sir Lancelot told the queen all, and how he was made to lie by her 'in the likeness of you, my lady the queen;' and so the queen held Sir Lancelot excused.

And as the book saith, King Arthur had been in France, and had warred upon the mighty King Claudas, and had won

[9] fitting	[13] suspended
[10] in	[14] dazzled
[11] dressed	[15] so that for a moment
[12] there	[16] went back to

much of his lands. And when the king was come again [17] he let cry [18] a great feast, that all lords and ladies of all England should be there but if it were [19] such as were rebellious against him.

And when Dame Elaine, the daughter of King Pelles, heard of this feast she yode to her father and required of him that he would give her leave to ride to that feast. The king answered and said,

'I will that ye go thither. But in any wise as ye love me and will have my blessing, look that ye be well beseen [20] the most richest wise, and look that ye spare not for no cost.[1] Ask and ye shall have all that needeth unto you.'

Then by the advice of Dame Brusen, her maiden, all thing was apparelled [2] unto the purpose, that there was never no lady richlier beseen.[20] So she rode with twenty knights and ten ladies and gentlewomen, to the number of an hundred horse. And when she came to Camelot King Arthur and Queen Guinevere said with all the knights that Dame Elaine was the fairest and the best beseen [20] lady that ever was seen in that court.

And anon as King Arthur wist that she was come, he met her and salewed her, and so did the most party of all the knights of the Round Table, both Sir Tristram, Sir Bleoberis, and Sir Gawain, and many more that I will not rehearse.[3]

But when Sir Lancelot saw her he was so ashamed, and that because he drew his sword to her on the morn after that he had lain by her, that he would not salew her nother speak with her. And yet Sir Lancelot thought that she was the fairest woman that ever he saw in his life-days.

But when Dame Elaine saw Sir Lancelot would not speak unto her she was so heavy [4] she weened her heart would have to-brast; [5] for wit you well, out of measure she loved him. And then Dame Elaine said unto her woman, Dame Brusen,

'The unkindness of Sir Lancelot slayeth mine heart near!'

'Ah! peace, madam,' said Dame Brusen, 'I shall undertake

---

[17] back
[18] proclaim
[19] except
[20] dressed
[1] spare no cost

[2] provided
[3] name
[4] sad
[5] would break

that this night he shall lie with you, an ye will hold you still.'

'That were me liefer,' said Dame Elaine, 'than all the gold that is aboven earth.'

'Let me deal,' said Dame Brusen.

So when Dame Elaine was brought unto the Queen either made other good cheer as by countenance,[6] but nothing with their hearts. But all men and women spake of the beauty of Dame Elaine.

And then it was ordained that Dame Elaine should sleep in a chamber nigh by the queen, and all under one roof. And so it was done as the king commanded. Then the queen sent for Sir Lancelot and bade him come to her chamber that night, 'other else,' said the queen, 'I am sure that ye will go to your lady's bed, Dame Elaine, by whom ye gat [7] Galahad.'

'Ah, madam!' said Sir Lancelot, 'never say ye so, for that [8] I did was against my will.'

'Then,' said the queen, 'look that ye come to me when I send for you.'

'Madam,' said Sir Lancelot, 'I shall not fail you, but I shall be ready at your commandment.'

So this bargain was soon not so [9] done and made between them but Dame Brusen knew it by her crafts, and told it unto her lady, Dame Elaine.

'Alas!' said she, 'how shall I do?'

'Let me deal,' said Dame Brusen, 'for [10] I shall bring him by the hand even to your bed, and he shall ween that I am Queen Guinevere's messenger.'

'Then well were me,' said Dame Elaine, 'for all the world I love not so much as I do Sir Lancelot.'

So when time came that all folks were to bed, Dame Brusen came to Sir Lancelot's bed's side and said,

'Sir Lancelot du Lake, sleep ye? My lady, Queen Guinevere, lieth and awaiteth upon you.'

'Ah, my fair lady!' said Sir Lancelot, 'I am ready to go with you whither ye will have me.'

So Sir Lancelot threw upon him a long gown, and so he took his sword in his hand. And then Dame Brusen took him

---

[6] in outward appearance
[7] begot
[8] that which
[9] no sooner
[10] and

by the finger and led him to her lady's bed, Dame Elaine, and then she departed and left them there in bed together. And wit you well this lady was glad, and so was Sir Lancelot, for he weened that he had had another in his arms.

Now leave we them kissing and clipping, as was a kindly [11] thing, and now speak we of Queen Guinevere that sent one of her women that she most trusted unto Sir Lancelot's bed. And when she came there she found the bed cold, and he was not therein; and so she came to the queen and told her all.

'Alas,' said the queen, 'where is that false knight become?'

So the queen was nigh out of her wit, and then she writhed and weltered as a mad woman, and might not sleep a four or a five hours.

Then Sir Lancelot had a condition that he used of custom,[12] to clatter [13] in his sleep and to speak often of his lady, Queen Guinevere. So Sir Lancelot had awaked as long as it had pleased him, and so by course of kind [14] he slept and Dame Elaine both. And in his sleep he talked and clattered [13] as a jay of the love that had been betwixt Queen Guinevere and him, and as he talked so loud the queen heard him thereas [15] she lay in her chamber. And when she heard him so clatter she was wroth out of measure, and for anger and pain wist not what to do, and then she coughed so loud that Sir Lancelot awaked. And anon he knew her hemming,[16] and then he knew well that he lay by the Queen Elaine, and therewith he leapt out of his bed as he had been a wood man,[17] in his shirt, and anon the queen met him in the floor; and thus she said:

'Ah, thou false traitor-knight! Look thou never abide in my court, and lightly that thou avoid my chamber! And not so hardy,[18] thou false traitor-knight, that evermore thou come in my sight!'

'Alas!' said Sir Lancelot.

And therewith he took such an heartly sorrow at her words that he fell down to the floor in a swoon. And therwithal Queen Guinevere departed.

And when Sir Lancelot awoke out of his swoon he leapt

[11] natural
[12] had a peculiar habit
[13] chatter (ed)
[14] as was natural
[15] where
[16] coughing
[17] madman
[18] be not so daring

out at a bay-window into a garden, and there with thorns he
was all to-scratched of [19] his visage and his body; and so he
ran forth he knew not whither, and was as wild-wood [20] as
ever was man. And so he ran two year, and never man had
grace to know him.[1]

Now turn we unto Queen Guinevere and to the fair Lady
Elaine, that when Dame Elaine heard the queen so rebuke
Sir Lancelot, and how also he swooned, and how he leapt out
at the bay-window, then she said unto Queen Guinevere,

'Madam, ye are greatly to blame for Sir Lancelot, for now
have ye lost him, for I saw and heard by his countenance that
he is mad for ever. And therefore, alas! madame, ye have
done great sin, and yourself great dishonour, for ye have a
lord royal of your own, and therefore it were your part to
love him; for there is no queen in this world that hath such
another king as ye have. And if ye were not, I might have
gotten the love of my lord Sir Lancelot; and great cause I
have to love him for he had my maidenhood, and by him I
have borne a fair son whose name is Sir Galahad. And he
shall be in his time the best knight of the world.'

'Well, Dame Elaine,' said the queen, 'as soon as it is daylight
I charge you to avoid [2] my court. And for the love you owe
unto Sir Lancelot discover [3] not his counsel,[4] for an ye do, it
will be his death.'

'As for that,' said Dame Elaine, 'I dare undertake he is
marred for ever, and that have you made. For nother ye nor
I are like to rejoice him, for he made the most piteous groans
when he leapt out at yonder bay-window that ever I heard
man make.' 'Alas,' said fair Elaine, and 'alas,' said the queen,
'for now I wot well that we have lost him for ever!'

So on the morn Dame Elaine took her leave to depart and
would no longer abide. Then King Arthur brought her on
her way with more than an hundred knights throughout a
forest. And by the way she told Sir Bors de Ganis all how it
betid that same night, and how Sir Lancelot leapt out at a
window araged out of his wit.

19 in
20 raving mad
1 the good fortune to recognize
him

2 leave
3 disclose
4 secret

'Alas!' then said Sir Bors, 'where is my lord Sir Lancelot become?'

'Sir,' said Dame Elaine, 'I wot ne'er.'

'Now, alas,' said Sir Bors, 'betwixt you both ye have destroyed a good knight.'

'As for me, sir,' said Dame Elaine, 'I said never nother did thing that should in any wise displease him. But with the rebuke, sir, that Queen Guinevere gave him I saw him swoon to the earth. And when he awoke he took his sword in his hand, naked save his shirt, and leap out at a window with the grisliest groan that ever I heard man make.'

'Now farewell,' said Sir Bors unto Dame Elaine, 'and hold my lord King Arthur with a tale as long as ye can, for I will turn again [5] unto Queen Guinevere and give her an hete.[6] And I require you, as ever ye will have my service, make good watch and espy if ever it may happen you to see my lord Sir Lancelot.'

'Truly,' said Dame Elaine, 'I shall do all that I may do, for I would as fain know and wit where he is become as you or any of his kin or Queen Guinevere, and great cause enough have I thereto as well as any other. And wit you well,' said fair Elaine to Sir Bors, 'I would lose my life for him rather than he should be hurt.'

'Madam,' said Dame Brusen, 'let Sir Bors depart and hie him as fast as he may to seek Sir Lancelot, for I warn you, he is clean out of his mind; and yet he shall be well holpen an but by miracle.'

Then wept Dame Elaine, and so did Sir Bors de Ganis; and anon they departed. And Sir Bors rode straight unto Queen Guinevere, and when she saw Sir Bors she wept as she were wood.[7]

'Now, fie on your weeping!' said Sir Bors de Ganis. 'For ye weep never but when there is no boot.[8] Alas!' said Sir Bors, 'that ever Sir Lancelot or any of his blood ever saw you, for now have ye lost the best knight of our blood, and he that was all our leader and our succour. And I dare say and make it good that all kings christened nother heathen may

---

[5] return
[6] tell her I disapprove of her behaviour
[7] mad
[8] it is of no use

not find such a knight, for to speak of his nobleness and courtesy, with his beauty and his gentleness. Alas!' said Sir Bors, 'what shall we do that be of his blood?'

'Alas!' said Sir Ector de Maris, and 'Alas!' said Sir Lionel.

And when the queen heard they say so she fell to the earth in a dead swoon. And then Sir Bors took her up and dawed [9] her, and when she awaked she kneeled afore those three knights and held up both her hands and besought them to seek him: 'And spare not for no goods but that [10] he be founden, for I wot well that he is out of his mind.'

And Sir Bors, Sir Ector and Sir Lionel departed from the queen, for they might not abide no longer for sorrow. And then the queen sent them treasure enough for their expense, and so they took their horses and their armour and departed. And then they rode from country to country, in forests and in wilderness and in wastes, and ever they laid watch both at forests and at all manner of men [11] as they rode, to hearken and to spare after [12] him, as he that [13] was a naked man in his shirt with a sword in his hand.

And thus they rode nigh a quarter of a year, long and overthwart, [14] and never could hear word of him, and wit you well these three knights were passing sorry. And so at the last Sir Bors and his fellows met with a knight that hight Sir Melion de Tartare.

'Now, fair knight,' said Sir Bors, 'whither be ye away?' (For they knew either other aforetime.)

'Sir,' said Sir Melion, 'I am in the way to the court of King Arthur.'

'Then we pray you,' said Sir Bors, 'that ye woll tell my lord Arthur and my lady Queen Guinevere and all the fellowship of the Round Table that we cannot in no [15] wise hear tell where Sir Lancelot is become.' [16]

Then Sir Melion departed from them and said that he would tell the king and the queen and all the fellowship of the Round Table as they had desired him. And when Sir Melion

---

[9] revived
[10] whatever the cost do not cease looking for him until
[11] and wherever they found a man to ask
[12] look for
[13] saying that he
[14] in all directions
[15] can in no
[16] has gone

came to the court he told the king and the queen and all the fellowship as they had desired him, how Sir Bors had said of Sir Lancelot.

Then Sir Gawain, Sir Uwain, Sir Sagramore le Desirous, Sir Aglovale, and Sir Perceval de Galis took upon them by the great desire of the king, and in especial by the queen, to seek all England, Wales and Scotland to find Sir Lancelot. And with them rode eighteen knights more to bear them fellowship,[17] and wit you well they lacked no manner of spending; [18] and so were they three-and-twenty knights.

Now turn we unto Sir Lancelot and speak we of his care and woe, and what pain he there endured; for cold, hunger and thirst he had plenty, and [19] . . . suffered and endured many sharp showers, that ever ran wild-wood from place to place and lived by fruit and such as he might get, and drank water two year; and other clothing had he but little but his shirt and his breek. Thus as Sir Lancelot wandered here and there he came into a fair meadow where he found a pavilion. And thereby upon a tree hung a white shield, and two swords hung thereby, and two spears leaned thereby to a tree. And when Sir Lancelot saw the swords, anon he leapt to the one sword, and clutched that sword in his hand and drew it out. And then he lashed at the shield, that all the meadow rang of the dints, that he gave such a noise as ten knights had fought together.

Then came forth a dwarf, and leap unto Sir Lancelot, and would have had the sword out of his hand. And then Sir Lancelot took him by the both shoulders and threw him unto the ground, that he fell upon his neck and had nigh broken it. And therewithal the dwarf cried help.

Then there came forth a likely [20] knight and well apparelled in scarlet furred with miniver.[1] And anon as he saw Sir Lancelot he deemed that he should be out of his wit, and then he said with fair speech,

'Good man, lay down that sword! For as meseemeth thou

---

[17] keep them company
[18] money to spend
[19] *In M this is followed by an account of Perceval's adventures (O, pp. 809–817), which it seems* *legitimate to omit since there is evidence to show (O, p. 1515) that M himself was doubtful about its relevance to the story.*
[20] handsome

hadst more need of a sleep and of warm clothes than to wield that sword.'

'As for that,' said Sir Lancelot, 'come not too nigh, for an thou do, wit thou well I will slay thee.'

And when the knight of the pavilion saw that, he start backward into his pavilion. And then the dwarf armed him lightly,[2] and so the knight thought by force and might to have taken the sword from Sir Lancelot. And so he came stepping upon him, and when Sir Lancelot saw him come so armed with his sword in his hand, then Sir Lancelot flew to him with such a might and smote him upon the helm such a buffet that the stroke troubled[3] his brain, and therewithal the sword brake in three. And the knight fell to the earth and seemed as he had been dead, the blood brasting out of his mouth, nose, and ears.

And then Sir Lancelot ran into the pavilion, and rushed even[4] into the warm bed. And there was a lady that lay in that bed; and anon she gat her smock and ran out of the pavilion, and when she saw her lord lie at the ground like to be dead, then she cried and wept as she had been mad. And so with her noise[5] the knight awaked out of his swough, and looked up weakly with his eyen.

And then he asked where was that mad man that had given him such a buffet, 'for such a one had I never of man's hand.'

'Sir,' said the dwarf, 'it is not your worship to hurt him, for he is a man out of his wit; and doubt ye not he hath been a man of great worship, and for some heartly[6] sorrow that he hath taken, he is fallen mad. And meseemeth,' said the dwarf, 'that he resembleth much unto Sir Lancelot, for him I saw at the tournament of Lonezep.'

'Jesu defend,' said that knight, 'that ever that noble knight, Sir Lancelot, should be in such a plight! But whatsomever he be,' said the knight, 'harm will I none do him.'

And this knight's name was Sir Blyaunt, the which said unto the dwarf,

'Go thou fast on horseback unto my brother Sir Selivaunt,

---

[1] trimmed with ermine   [4] straight
[2] swiftly   [5] cries
[3] injured   [6] grievous

which is at the Castle Blank, and tell him of mine adventure, and bid him bring with him an horse-litter. And then will we bear this knight unto my castle.'

So the dwarf rode fast, and he came again [7] and brought Sir Selivaunt with him, and six men with an horse-litter. And so they took up the feather bed with Sir Lancelot, and so carried all away with them unto the Castle Blank, and he never awaked till he was within the castle. And then they bound his hands and his feet, and gave him good meats and good drinks, and brought him again to his strength and his fairness.[8] But in his wit they could not bring him nother to know himself. And thus was Sir Lancelot there more than a year and an half, honestly arrayed [9] and fair faren [10] withal.

Then upon a day this lord of that castle, Sir Blyaunt, took his arms on horseback with a spear to seek adventures. And as he rode in a forest there met him two knights adventurous, the one was Sir Breuse Saunce Pity, and his brother, Sir Bartelot. And these two ran both at once on Sir Blyaunt and brake their spears upon his body. And then they drew their swords and made great battle, and fought long together. But at the last Sir Blyaunt was sore wounded, and felt himself faint, and anon he fled on horseback toward his castle.

And as they came hurling under the castle there was Sir Lancelot at a window, and saw how two knights laid upon Sir Blyaunt with their swords. And when Sir Lancelot saw that, yet as wood as he was he was sorry for his lord, Sir Blyaunt. And then in a braid [11] Sir Lancelot brake his chains off his legs and off his arms, and in the breaking he hurt his hands sore; and so Sir Lancelot ran out at a postern, and there he met with those two knights that chased Sir Blyaunt. And there he pulled down Sir Bartelot with his bare hands from his horse, and therewithal he wroth out [12] the sword out of his hand, and so he leap unto Sir Breuse and gave him such a buffet upon the head that he tumbled backward over his horse croup.[13]

And when Sir Bartelot saw his brother have such a buffet

---

7 back
8 good looks
9 decently clad
10 well-treated

11 sudden movement
12 wrenched
13 horse's hind-quarters

he gat a spear in his hand, and would have run Sir Lancelot through. And that saw Sir Blyaunt, and struck off the hand of Sir Bartelot. And then Sir Breuse and Sir Bartelot gat their horses and fled away as fast as they might.

So when Sir Selivaunt came and saw what Sir Lancelot had done for his brother, then he thanked God, and so did his brother, that ever they did him any good. But when Sir Blyaunt saw that Sir Lancelot was hurt with the breaking of his irons, then was he heavy [14] that ever he bound him.

'I pray you, brother, Sir Selivaunt, bind him no more, for he is happy [15] and gracious.' [16]

Then they made great joy of Sir Lancelot, and so he abode thereafter an half year and more.

And so on a morn Sir Lancelot was ware where came a great boar with many hounds after him, but the boar was so big there might no hounds tarry [17] him. And so the hunters came after, blowing their horns, both upon horseback and some upon foot, and then Sir Lancelot was ware where one alight and tied his horse till a tree, and leaned his spear against the tree. So there came Sir Lancelot and found the horse, and a good sword tied to the saddle-bow; and anon Sir Lancelot leap into the saddle and gat that spear in his hand, and then he rode fast after the boar.

And anon he was ware where he sat, and his arse to a rock, fast by an hermitage. And then Sir Lancelot ran at the boar with his spear, and all to-shivered his spear. And therewith the boar turned him lightly, and rove [18] out the lungs and the heart of the horse, that Sir Lancelot fell to the earth; and, or ever he might [19] get from his horse, the boar smote him on the brawn [20] of the thigh up unto the hough bone.[1] And then Sir Lancelot was wroth, and up he gat upon his feet, and took his sword and smote off the boar's head at one stroke.

And therewithal came out the hermit and saw him have such a wound. Anon he meaned him,[2] and would have had him home unto his hermitage. But when Sir Lancelot heard

[14] filled with regret
[15] harmless
[16] kind-hearted
[17] stay
[18] ripped
[19] before he could
[20] flesh
[1] back part of the knee-joint
[2] pitied him

him speak, he was so wroth with his wound that he ran upon
the hermit to have slain him. Then the hermit ran away, and
when Sir Lancelot might not overget [3] him, he threw his
sword after him, for he might no further [4] for bleeding. Then
the hermit turned again [5] and asked Sir Lancelot how he was
hurt.

'Ah, my fellow,' said Sir Lancelot, 'this boar hath bitten me
sore.'

'Then come ye with me,' said the hermit, 'and I shall heal
you.'

'Go thy way,' said Sir Lancelot, 'and deal [6] not with me!'

Then the hermit ran his way, and there he met with a
goodly knight with many men.

'Sir,' said the hermit, 'here is fast by my place the goodliest
man that I ever saw, and he is sore wounded with a boar, and
yet he hath slain the boar. But well I wot,' said the good man,
'an he be not holpen, he shall die of that wound, and that
were great pity.'

Then that knight at the desire of the hermit gat a cart, and
therein he put the boar and Sir Lancelot, for he was so feeble
that they might right easily deal with him. And so Sir Lancelot was brought into the hermitage, and there the hermit
healed him of his wound. But the hermit might not find him
his sustenance, so he impaired [7] and waxed feeble, both of
body and of his wit: for default of sustenance he waxed
more wooder [8] than he was aforetime.

And then upon a day Sir Lancelot ran his way into the
forest; and by the adventure he came to the city of Corbin
where Dame Elaine was, that bare Galahad, Sir Lancelot's
son. And when he was entered into the town he ran through
the town to the castle; and then all the young men of that
city ran after Sir Lancelot, and there they threw turves at
him and gave him many sad strokes. And even as Sir Lancelot might reach any of them, he threw them so that they
would never come in his hands no more, for of some he brake
the legs and arms.

And so he fled into the castle, and then came out knights

[3] overtake
[4] could run no more
[5] back
[6] trouble
[7] grew worse
[8] more mad

and squires and rescued Sir Lancelot. When they beheld him and looked upon his person, they thought they saw never so goodly [9] a man. And when they saw so many wounds upon him, they deemed that he had been a man of worship. And then they ordained him clothes to his body, and straw and litter under the gate of the castle to lie in. And so every day they would throw him meat and set him drink, but there was but few that would bring him meat to his hands.

So it befell that King Pelles had a nephew whose name was Castor; and so he desired of the king to be made knight, and at his own request the king made him knight at the feast of Candlemas. And when Sir Castor was made knight, that same day he gave many gowns. And then Sir Castor sent for the fool, which was Sir Lancelot; and when he came afore Sir Castor, he gave Sir Lancelot a robe of scarlet and all that longed unto him.[10] And when Sir Lancelot was so arrayed like a knight he was the seemliest [11] man in all the court, and none so well made.

So when he saw his time [12] he went into the garden, and there he laid him down by a well and slept. And so at after noon Dame Elaine and her maidens came into the garden to sport them. And as they roamed up and down one of Dame Elaine's maidens espied where lay a goodly [9] man by the well sleeping.

'Peace,' said Dame Elaine, 'and say no word, but show me that man where he lieth.'

So anon she brought Dame Elaine where he lay. And when that she beheld him, anon she fell in remembrance of him, and knew him verily for Sir Lancelot. And therewithal she fell on-weeping so heartily that she sank even [13] to the earth. And when she had thus wept a great while, then she arose and called her maidens and said she was sick. And so she yode out of the garden as straight to her father as she could, and there she took him by herself apart; and then she said,

'Ah, my dear father, now I have need of your help, and but if that ye help me now, farewell my good days forever!'

'What is that, daughter?' said King Pelles.

---

[9] handsome
[10] was fitting for him to wear
[11] handsomest
[12] opportunity
[13] fell down

'In your garden I was to sport me, and there, by the well
I found Sir Lancelot du Lake sleeping.'

'I may not believe it!' said King Pelles.

'Truly, sir, he is there!' she said. 'And meseemeth he should
be yet distract [14] out of his wit.'

'Then hold you still,' said the king, 'and let me deal.'

Then the king called unto him such as he most trusted, a
four persons, and Dame Elaine, his daughter, and Dame Brusen, her servant. And when they came to the well and beheld
Sir Lancelot, anon Dame Brusen said to the king,

'We must be wise how we deal with him, for this knight
is out of his mind, and if we awake him rudely, what he will
do we all know not. And therefore abide ye a while and I
shall throw an enchantment upon him, that he shall not awake
of [15] an hour.'

And so she did, and then the king commanded that all
people should avoid,[16] that none should be in that way
thereas [17] the king would come. And so when this was done
these four men and these ladies laid hand on Sir Lancelot, and
so they bare him into a tower, and so into a chamber where
was the holy vessel of the Sankgreall. And before that holy
vessel Sir Lancelot was laid. And there came an holy man and
unhilled [18] that vessel, and so by miracle and by virtue of that
holy vessel Sir Lancelot was healed and recovered.

And as soon as he was awakened he groaned and sighed, and
complained him sore of his woodness and strokes that he had
had. And as soon as Sir Lancelot saw King Pelles and Dame
Elaine, he waxed ashamed and said thus:

'Ah, Lord Jesu, how came I hither? For God's sake, my
fair lord, let me wit how that I came hither!'

'Sir,' said Dame Elaine, 'into this country ye came like a
mazed man,[19] clean out of your wit. And here have ye been
kept as a fool, and no creature here knew what ye were, until
by fortune a maiden of mine brought me unto you whereas [20]
ye lay sleeping by a well. And anon as I verily beheld you I
knew you. Then I told my father, and so were ye brought

[14] distracted
[15] for
[16] withdraw
[17] where

[18] uncovered
[19] man out of his senses
[20] where

afore this holy vessel, and by the virtue of it thus were ye healed.'

'Ah Jesu, mercy!' said Sir Lancelot. 'If this be sooth, how many be there that knoweth of my woodness?' [1]

'So God me help,' said Dame Elaine, 'no more but my father, and I, and Dame Brusen.'

'Now for Christ's love,' said Sir Lancelot, 'keep it counsel,[2] and let no man know it in the world. For I am sore ashamed that I have been misfortuned,[3] for I am banished the country of England.'

And so Sir Lancelot lay more than a fortnight or ever that he might [4] stir for soreness. And then upon a day he said unto Dame Elaine these words,

'Fair Lady Elaine, for your sake I have had much care and anguish, it needeth not to rehearse [5] it, ye know how. Notwithstanding I know well I have done foul to you when that I drew my sword to you to have slain you upon the morn after when that I had lain with you. And all was for the cause that ye and Dame Brusen made me for to lie by you maugre mine head.[6] And as ye say, Sir Galahad, your son, was begotten.'

'That is truth,' said Dame Elaine.

'Then will ye for my sake,' said Sir Lancelot, 'go ye unto your father and get me a place of [7] him wherein I may dwell? For in the court of King Arthur may I never come.'

'Sir,' said Dame Elaine, 'I will live and die with you, only for your sake; and if my life might not avail you and my death might avail you, wit you well I would die for your sake. And I will to my father, and I am right sure there is nothing that I can desire of him but I shall have it. And where ye be, my lord Sir Lancelot, doubt ye not but I will be with you with all the service that I may do.'

So forthwithal she went to her father and said,

'Sir, my lord Sir Lancelot desireth to be here by you in some castle of yours.'

'Well, daughter,' said the king, 'sith it is his desire to abide

---

[1] madness
[2] a secret
[3] of my misfortune
[4] before he could
[5] describe
[6] against my will
[7] from

in these marches he shall be in the Castle of Blyaunt, and there shall ye be with him, and twenty of the fairest young ladies that been in this country, and they shall be all of the greatest blood [8] in this country; and ye shall have twenty knights with you. For, daughter, I will that ye wit we all be honoured by the blood [9] of Sir Lancelot.'

Then went Dame Elaine unto Sir Lancelot, and told him all how her father had devised. Then came a knight which was called Sir Castor, that was nephew unto King Pelles, and he came unto Sir Lancelot, and asked him what was his name.

'Sir,' said Sir Lancelot, 'my name is Le Chevalier Ill Mafete,[10] that is to say, "the knight that hath trespassed." '

'Sir,' said Sir Castor, 'it may well be so, but ever meseemeth your name should be Sir Lancelot du Lake, for or now I have seen you.'

'Sir,' said Lancelot, 'ye are not gentle,[11] for I put a case [12] my name were Sir Lancelot, and that it list me not to discover my name, what should it grieve you here to keep my counsel [13] and ye not hurt thereby? But wit you well, an ever it lie in my power, I shall grieve you, an ever I meet with you in my way!'

Then Sir Castor kneeled down and besought Sir Lancelot of mercy: 'for I shall never utter what ye be while that ye are in these parts.'

Then Sir Lancelot pardoned him. And so King Pelles with twenty knights, and Dame Elaine with her twenty ladies, rode unto the Castle of Blyaunt that stood in an island beclosed environ [14] with a fair water deep and large. And when they were there Sir Lancelot let call it The Joyous Isle; and there was he called none otherwise but Le Chevalier Mafete, 'the knight that hath trespassed'.

Then Sir Lancelot let make him a shield all of sable, and a queen crowned in the midst,[15] all silver, and a knight clean [16] armed kneeling afore her. And every day once, for any mirths

---

[8] nobility
[9] noble ancestry
[10] F: '*li chevaliers Mesfait*.' It is *not clear whether M's 'Ill' is a rendering of the French prefix 'mes' or whether the whole phrase is a corruption (perhaps deliberate) of 'li chevaliers qui mesfist.'*
[11] courteous
[12] for supposing
[13] secret
[14] surrounded on all sides
[15] centre
[16] fully

that all the ladies might make him, he would once every day look toward the realm of Logres, where King Arthur and Queen Guinevere was, and then would he fall upon a-weeping as his heart should to-brast.

So it befell that time Sir Lancelot heard of a jousting fast by, within three leagues. Then he called unto him a dwarf, and he bade him go unto that jousting: 'And or ever [17] the knights depart, look that thou make there a cry,[18] in hearing of all knights, that there is one knight in Joyous Isle, which is the Castle of Blyaunt, and say his name is Le Chevalier Mafete, that will joust against knights all that will come. And who that putteth that knight to the worse, he shall have a fair maiden and a gerfalcon.'

So when his cry [18] was cried, unto Joyous Isle drew the number of five hundred knights. And wit you well there was never seen in King Arthur's day one knight that did so much deeds of arms as Sir Lancelot did those three days together.[19] For, as the book maketh truly mention, he had the better of all the five hundred knights, and there was not one slain of them. And after that Sir Lancelot made them all a great feast.

And in the meanwhile came Sir Perceval de Galis and Sir Ector de Maris under that castle [20] which was called the Joyous Isle. And as they beheld that gay castle they would have gone to that castle, but they might not for the broad water, and bridge could they find none. Then were they ware on the other side where stood a lady with a sparhawk [1] on her hand, and Sir Perceval called unto her, and asked that lady who was in that castle.

'Fair knights,' she said, 'here within this castle is the fairest lady in this land, and her name is Dame Elaine. Also we have in this castle one of the fairest knights and the mightiest man that is, I dare say, living, and he calleth himself Le Chevalier Mafete.'

'How came he into these marches?' [2] said Sir Perceval.

'Truly,' said the damsel, 'he came into this country like a mad man, with dogs and boys chasing him through the city of Corbin, and by the holy vessel of the Sankgreall he was

[17] before
[18] proclamation
[19] during those three days

[20] to the walls of that castle
[1] sparrowhawk
[2] this land

brought into his wit again. But he will not do battle with no knight but by undern[3] or by noon. And if ye list to come into the castle,' said the lady, 'ye must ride unto the further side of the castle, and there shall ye find a vessel that will bear you and your horse.'

Then they departed and came unto the vessel; and then Sir Perceval alight, and said unto Sir Ector de Maris,

'Ye shall abide me here until that I wit what manner a knight he is. For it were shame unto us, inasmuch as he is but one knight, an we should both do battle with him.'

'Do ye as ye list,' said Sir Ector, 'and here I shall abide you until that I hear of you.'

Then passed Sir Perceval the water, and when he came to the castle gate he said unto the porter,

'Go thou to the good knight of this castle and tell him here is come an errant knight to joust with him.'

Then the porter yode in and came again[4] and bade him ride into the common place[5] thereas[6] the jousting shall be, 'where lords and ladies may behold you.'

And so anon as Sir Lancelot had a warning he was soon ready, and there Sir Perceval and Sir Lancelot were come both. They encountered with such a might, and their spears were so rude,[7] that both the horses and the knights fell to the ground. Then they avoided[8] their horses, and flung[9] out their noble swords, and hew away many cantles[10] of their shields, and so hurtled together with their shields like two boars, and either wounded other passing sore. And so at the last Sir Perceval spake first, when they had foughten there long, more than two hours:

'Now fair knight,' said Sir Perceval, 'I require you of[11] your knighthood to tell me your name, for I met never with such another knight.'

'Sir, as for my name,' said Sir Lancelot, 'I will not hide it from you, but my name is Le Chevalier Mafete. Now tell me your name,' said Sir Lancelot, 'I require you.'

---

[3] nine o'clock in the morning
[4] back
[5] open place
[6] where
[7] heavy
[8] dismounted from
[9] drew
[10] pieces
[11] by

'Truly,' said Sir Perceval, 'my name is Sir Perceval de Galis, that was brother unto the good knight Sir Lamorak de Galis, and King Pellinore was our father, and Sir Aglovale is my brother.'

'Alas,' said Sir Lancelot, 'what have I done to fight with you which are a knight of the Table Round! And sometime I was your fellow.'

And therewithal Sir Lancelot kneeled down upon his knees and threw away his shield and his sword from him. When Sir Perceval saw him do so he marvelled what he meaned, and then he said thus:

'Sir knight, whatsomever ye be, I require you upon the high Order of Knighthood to tell me your true name.'

Then he answered and said, 'So God me help, my name is Sir Lancelot du Lake, King Ban's son of Benoy.'

'Alas!' then said Sir Perceval, 'what have I now done? For I was sent by the queen for to seek you, and so I have sought you nigh this two year, and yonder is Sir Ector de Maris, your brother, which abideth me on the yonder side of the water. And therefore, for God's sake,' said Sir Perceval, 'forgive me mine offences that I have here done.'

'Sir, it is soon forgiven,' said Sir Lancelot.

Then Sir Perceval sent for Sir Ector de Maris; and when Sir Lancelot had a sight of him he ran unto him and took him in his arms; and then Sir Ector kneeled down, and either wept upon other, that all men had pity to behold them.

Then came forth Dame Elaine. And she made them great cheer as might be made, and there she told Sir Ector and Sir Perceval how and in what manner Sir Lancelot came into that country and how he was healed. And there it was known how long Sir Lancelot was with Sir Blyaunt and with Sir Selyvaunt, and how he first met with them, and how he departed from them because he was hurt with a boar, and how the hermit healed him of his great wound, and how that he came to the city of Corbin.

. . . So it befell [12] on a day that Sir Ector and Sir Perceval came unto Sir Lancelot and asked of him what he would do,

---

[12] *The passage omitted here (O, pp. 830–1) contains a brief account of how Bors found his son Elyne le Blank and brought him to Arthur's court.*

and whether he would go with them unto King Arthur.

'Nay,' said Sir Lancelot, 'that may I not do by no mean,[13] for I was so vengeably defended [14] the court that I cast me never to come there more.'

'Sir,' said Sir Ector, 'I am your brother, and ye are the man in the world that I love most. And if I understood that it were your disworship,[15] ye may understand that I would never counsel you thereto. But King Arthur and all his knights, and in especial [16] Queen Guinevere, maketh such dole and sorrow for you that it is marvel [17] to hear and see. And ye must remember the great worship and renown that ye be of, how that ye have been more spoken of than any other knight that is now living; for there is none that beareth the name now but ye and Sir Tristram. And therefore, brother,' said Sir Ector, 'make you ready to ride to the court with us. And I daresay and make it good,' said Sir Ector, 'it hath cost my lady the queen twenty thousand pounds, the seeking of you.'

'Well brother,' said Sir Lancelot, 'I will do after your counsel and ride with you.'

So then they took their horses and made ready, and anon they took their leave at King Pelles and at Dame Elaine. And when Sir Lancelot should depart Dame Elaine made great sorrow.

'My lord, Sir Lancelot,' said Dame Elaine, 'this same feast of Pentecost shall your son and mine, Galahad, be made knight, for he is now fully fifteen winter old.'

'Madam, do as ye list,' said Sir Lancelot, 'and God give him grace to prove a good knight.'

'As for that,' said Dame Elaine, 'I doubt not he shall prove the best man of his kin except one.'

'Then shall he be a good man enough,' said Sir Lancelot.

So anon they departed, and within fifteen days' journey they came unto Camelot, that is in English called Winchester.[18] And when Sir Lancelot was come among them, the king and all the knights made great joy of his homecoming.

---

13 I cannot possibly do so
14 cruelly forbidden
15 it would disgrace you
16 and even more
17 dreadful
18 *See below*, The Fair Maid of Astolat, *note 1.*

And there Sir Perceval and Sir Ector de Maris began and told the whole adventures: how Sir Lancelot had been out of his mind in the time of his absence, and how he called himself Le Chevalier Mafete, 'the knight that had trespassed;' and in three days within Joyous Isle Sir Lancelot smote down five hundred knights. And ever as Sir Ector and Sir Perceval told these tales of Sir Lancelot, Queen Guinevere wept as she should have died. Then the queen made him great cheer.

'Ah, Jesu!' said King Arthur, 'I marvel for what cause ye, Sir Lancelot, went out of your mind. For I and many other deem it was for the love of fair Elaine, the daughter of King Pelles, by whom ye are noised [19] that ye have gotten a child, and his name is Galahad. And men say that he shall do many marvellous things.'

'My lord,' said Sir Lancelot, 'if I did any folly I have that [20] I sought.'

And therewithal the king spake no more. But all Sir Lancelot's kinsmen knew for whom he went out of his mind. And then there was made great feasts, and great joy was there among them. And all lords and ladies made great joy when they heard that Sir Lancelot was come again unto the court.

[19] it is said   [20] what

The Holy Grail

Now saith the tale that Sir Galahad rode many journeys in vain, and at last he came to the abbey where King Mordrains was. And when he heard that, he thought he would abide to see him.

And so upon the morn, when he had heard mass, Sir Galahad came unto King Mordrains. And anon the king saw him, which had lain blind of long time, and then he dressed him against him [1] and said,

'Sir Galahad, the servant of Jesu Christ and very [2] knight, whose coming I have abiden long, now embrace me and let me rest on thy breast, so that I may rest [3] between thine arms! For thou art a clean virgin above all knights, as the flower of the lily in whom virginity is signified. And thou art the rose which is the flower of all good virtue, and in colour of fire. For the fire of the Holy Ghost is taken [4] so in thee that my flesh, which was all dead of oldness, is become again young.'

When Galahad heard these words, then he embraced him and all his body. Then said he,[5]

'Fair Lord Jesu Christ, now I have my will! Now I require Thee, in this point [6] that I am in, that Thou come and visit me.'

And anon Our Lord heard his prayer, and therewith the soul departed from the body. And then Sir Galahad put him in the earth as a king ought to be, and so departed and came into a perilous forest where he found the well which boiled with great waves, as the tale telleth tofore.[7]

---

[1] rose to meet him
[2] true
[3] die. Cf. F: 'si que je puisse trespasser entre tes bras.'
[4] burning. Cf. F: 'le feu du Saint Esperit est si en toy espris' (= 'aflame').
[5] = King Mordrains
[6] state
[7] See note 11.

And as soon as Sir Galahad set his hand thereto it ceased, so that it brent no more, and anon the heat departed away. And cause why it brent, it was a sign of lechery that was that time much used. But that heat might not abide his pure virginity. And so this was taken in the country for a miracle, and so ever after was it called Galahad's Well.

So by adventure he came unto the country of Gore, and into the abbey where Sir Lancelot had been toforehand and found the tomb of King Bagdemagus; but he was founder[8] thereof.[9] For[10] there was the tomb of Joseph of Arimathea's son and the tomb of Simeon, where Lancelot had failed.[11] Then he looked into a croft under the minster, and there he saw a tomb which brent full marvellously. Then asked he the brethren what it was.

'Sir,' said they, 'a marvellous adventure that may not be brought to an end but by him that passeth of bounty[12] and of knighthood all them of the Round Table.'

'I would,' said Sir Galahad, 'that ye would bring me thereto.'

'Gladly,' said they, and so led him till a cave. And he went down upon greses[13] and came unto the tomb. And so the flaming failed, and the fire staunched which many a day had been great.

Then came there a voice which said,

'Much are ye beholden to thank God which hath given you a good hour,[14] that ye may draw out the souls of earthly pain and to put them into the joys of Paradise. Sir, I am of your kindred, which hath dwelled in this heat this three hundred winter and four-and-fifty to be purged of the sin that I did against Arimathea Joseph.'

Then Sir Galahad took the body in his arms and bare it into the minster. And that night lay Sir Galahad in the abbey; and on the morn he gave him his service and put him in the earth before the high altar.

---

[8] finder

[9] *The repetition is puzzling and may be due to a fault in the text.*

[10] And

[11] *This is a reference to an episode familiar to readers of the French Prose Lancelot (cf. The Vulgate Version of the Arthurian Romances, ed. Sommer, IV, 175–7)* but not to readers of M. *The same may be said of the reference in the previous paragraph to the boiling fountain (cf. ibid., V, 244–8).*

[12] excellence

[13] steps

[14] good fortune ('*bon eur*' mistaken for '*bonne heure*')

So departed he from thence, and commended the brethren
to God, and so he rode five days till that he came to the
Maimed King. And ever followed Perceval the five days [15]
asking where he had been, and so one told him how the
adventures of Logres were achieved. So on a day it befell that
he came out of a great forest, and there they [16] met at trav-
erse [17] with Sir Bors which rode alone. It is no need to ask
if they were glad! And so he salewed them, and they yielded
to him [18] honour and good adventure, and everych told other
how they had sped. Then said Sir Bors,

'It is more than a year and a half that I ne lay [19] ten times
where men dwelled, but in wild forests and in mountains.
But God was ever my comfort.'

Then rode they a great while till they came to the castle of
Corbenic. And when they were entered within, King Pelles
knew them. So there was great joy, for he wist well by their
coming that they had fulfilled the Sankgreall.[20]

Then Eliazar, King Pelles' son, brought tofore them the
broken sword wherewith Joseph was stricken through the
thigh. Then Bors set his hand thereto to essay if he might
have sowded [1] it again; but it would not be. Then he took
it to Perceval, but he had no more power thereto than he.

'Now have ye it again,' said Sir Perceval unto Sir Galahad,
'for an it be ever achieved by any bodily man, ye must do
it.'

And then he took the pieces and set them together, and
seemed to them as it had never be broken, and as well as it was
first forged. And when they within espied that the adventure
of the sword was achieved, then they gave the sword to Sir
Bors, for it might no better be set,[2] for he was so good a
knight and a worthy man.

And a little before even the sword [3] arose, great and mar-

---

[15] *i.e. Perceval followed Galahad.
In F they do not part company
for five years.*
[16] = Perceval and Galahad
[17] crossways
[18] wished him in return
[19] have not lain
[20] F: *'they knew that the adventures of the castle would come to
an end' (fauldroient). M antici-*
pates the completion of the quest
by altering both the tense and the
meaning of the verb.
[1] soldered
[2] employed. F: *emploiee.*
[3] *This should be 'a wind.' cf. F:
'ung vent leva grant et merveil-
leux.' M misread 'ung vent' as 'un
gleve' — an easy slip when the two
words are not properly divided.*

vellous, and was full of great heat, that many men fell for
dread. And anon alight a voice among them and said,

'They that ought not to sit at the table of Our Lord Jesu
Christ, avoid [4] hence! For now there shall very [5] knights be
fed.'

So they went thence, all save King Pelles and Eliazar, his
son, which were holy men, and a maid which was his niece.
And so there abode these three knights and these three; else
were no more. And anon they saw knights all armed come in
at the hall door, and did off their helms and their arms, and
said unto Sir Galahad,

'Sir, we have hied right much for to be with you at this
table where the holy meat shall be departed.' [6]

Then said he, 'Ye be welcome! But of whence be ye?'

So three of them said they were of Gaul, and other three
said they were of Ireland, and other three said they were of
Denmark.

And so as they sat thus, there came out a bed of tree [7] of [8]
a chamber, which four gentlewomen brought; and in the bed
lay a good man sick, and had a crown of gold upon his head.
And there, in the midst [9] of the palace, they set him down
and went again. Then he lift up his head and said,

'Sir Galahad, good knight, ye be right welcome, for much
have I desired your coming! For in such pain and in such
anguish as I have no man else [10] might have suffered long.
But now I trust to God the term is come that my pain shall
be allayed, and so I shall pass out of this world, so as it was
promised me long ago.'

And therewith a voice said, 'There be two among you that
be not in the quest of the Sankgreall, and therefore departeth!'

Then King Pelles and his son departed. And therewithal
beseemed them [11] that there came an old man and four angels
from heaven, clothed in likeness of a bishop, and had a cross
in his hand. And these four angels bare him up in a chair and
set him down before the table of silver whereupon the Sank-

---

[4] withdraw
[5] true
[6] distributed (F: *departiz*)
[7] a wooden bed (F: *un lit de fust*)
[8] from
[9] centre
[10] no other man
[11] it seemed to them

greall was. And it seemed that he had in midst of [12] his forehead letters which said: 'See ye here Joseph, the first bishop
of Christendom, the same which Our Lord succoured [13] in
the city of Sarras in the spiritual palace.' Then the knights
marvelled, for that bishop was dead more than three hundred
year tofore.

'Ah, knights,' said he, 'marvel not, for I was sometime an
earthly man.'

So with that they heard the chamber door open, and there
they saw angels; and two bare candles of wax, and the third
bare a towel,[14] and the fourth a spear which bled marvellously,
that the drops fell within a box which he held with his other
hand. And anon they set the candles upon the table, and the
third the towel [14] upon the vessel, and the fourth the holy
spear even [15] upright upon the vessel.

And then the bishop made semblaunt as though he would
have gone to the sacring of a mass, and then he took an
ubblie [16] which was made in likeness of bread. And at the
lifting up there came a figure in likeness of a child, and the
visage was as red and as bright as any fire, and smote himself [17]
into the bread, that all they saw it that the bread was formed
of a fleshly man. And then he put it into the holy vessel
again, and then he did that longed [18] to a priest to do mass.

And then he went to Sir Galahad and kissed him, and bade
him go and kiss his fellows. And so he did anon.

'Now,' said he, 'the servants of Jesu Christ, ye shall be fed
afore this table with sweet meats that never knights yet
tasted.'

And when he had said he vanished away. And they set
them at the table in great dread and made their prayers. Then
looked they and saw a Man come out of the holy vessel that
had all the signs of the Passion of Jesu Christ, bleeding all
openly, and said,

'My knights and my servants and my true children which

[12] upon
[13] F has 'sacra' ('consecrated')
which makes better sense, but M
is often so attracted by the sound
of French words that he loses sight
of their meaning. Cf. O, pp. XLVI,
1525, 1542, 1548 and 1549.
[14] F: *une touaille* ('a veil') *de
vermeil samit*
[15] straight
[16] wafer, Host
[17] impressed its image
[18] what was fitting

be come out of deadly life into the spiritual life, I will no longer cover me from you, but ye shall see now a part of my secrets and of my hid things. Now holdeth and receiveth the high order and meat [19] which ye have so much desired.'

Then took He himself the holy vessel and came to Sir Galahad. And he kneeled down and received his Saviour. And after him so received all his fellows, and they thought it so sweet that it was marvellous to tell. Then said He to Sir Galahad,

'Son, wotest thou what I hold betwixt my hands?'

'Nay,' said he, 'but if ye tell me.'

'This is,' said He, 'the holy dish wherein I ate the lamb on Easter Day, and now hast thou seen that thou most desired to see. But yet hast thou not seen it so openly as thou shalt see it in the city of Sarras, in the spiritual palace. Therefore thou must go hence and bear with thee this holy vessel, for this night it shall depart from the realm of Logres, and it shall nevermore be seen here. And knowest thou wherefore? For he [20] is not served nother worshipped to his right [1] by them of this land, for they be turned to evil living, and therefore I shall disherit [2] them of the honour which I have done them. And therefore go ye three to-morn unto the sea, where ye shall find your ship ready, and with you take the sword with the strange girdles,[3] and no more with you but Sir Perceval and Sir Bors. Also I will that ye take with you of this blood of this spear for to anoint the Maimed King, both his legs and his body, and he shall have his heal.' [4]

'Sir,' said Galahad, 'why shall not these other fellows go with us?'

'For this cause: for right as I depart [5] my apostles one here and another there, so I will that ye depart.[5] And two of you shall die in my service, and one of you shall come again and tell tidings.'

Then gave He them His blessing and vanished away.

And Sir Galahad went anon to the spear which lay upon

---

[19] F: *la haute viande* ('the holy food')
[20] = the holy vessel (F: *il*)
[1] as it should be
[2] dispossess
[3] *A misreading of F's 'la nef ou tu preis l'espee' ('the ship from which you took the sword') as 'estranges renges.'*
[4] shall be restored
[5] separate

the table and touched the blood with his fingers, and came after to the maimed knight and anointed his legs and his body. And therewith he [6] clothed him anon, and start upon his feet out of his bed as an whole man, and thanked God that He had healed him. And anon he left the world and yielded himself to a place of religion of white monks, and was a full holy man.

And that same night, about midnight, came a voice among them which said,

'My sons, and not my chief sons,[7] my friends, and not mine enemies, go ye hence where ye hope best to do, and as I bade you do.'

'Ah, thanked be Thou, Lord, that Thou wilt vouchsafe [8] to call us Thy sons! Now may we well prove that we have not lost our pains.'

And anon in all haste they took their harness and departed; but the three knights of Gaul (one of them hight Claudine, King Claudas' son, and the other two were great gentlemen) then prayed Sir Galahad to everych of them, that an they come [9] to King Arthur's court, 'to salew my lord Sir Lancelot, my father, and them all of the Round Table'; and prayed them, an they came on that party,[10] not to forget it.

Right so departed Sir Galahad, and Sir Perceval and Sir Bors with him, and so they rode three days. And then they came to a rivage [11] and found the ship whereof the tale speaketh of tofore. And when they came to the board [12] they found in the midst of [13] the bed the table of silver which they had left with the Maimed King, and the Sankgreall which was covered with red samite.[14] Then were they glad to have such things in their fellowship; and so they entered and made great reverence thereto, and Sir Galahad fell on his knees and prayed long time to Our Lord, that at what time he asked he might pass out of this world. And so long he prayed till a voice said,

'Sir Galahad, thou shalt have thy request, and when thou

---

[6] = the maimed knight

[7] F: *Mi fil et ne mie mi fillastre* (= *stepsons*). *There seems to be no satisfactory explanation of the change from 'stepsons' to 'chief (= eldest?) sons'*

[8] M: whyghtsauff, 'be willing'

[9] Galahad then asked each one of the three knights of Gaul (. . .), if they, etc.

[10] to that country

[11] shore

[12] on board

[13] upon

[14] rich silk

asketh the death of thy body thou shalt have it, and then shalt thou have the life of thy soul.'

Then Sir Perceval heard him a little, and prayed him of [15] fellowship that was between them wherefore he asked such things.

'Sir, that shall I tell you,' said Sir Galahad. 'This other day, when we saw a part of the adventures of the Sankgreall, I was in such a joy of heart that I trow never man was that was earthly. And therefore I wot well, when my body is dead, my soul shall be in great joy to see the Blessed Trinity every day, and the majesty of Our Lord Jesu Christ.'

And so long were they in the ship that they said to Galahad,

'Sir, in this bed ye ought to lie, for so saith the letters.'

And so he laid him down, and slept a great while. And when he awaked he looked tofore him and saw the city of Sarras. And as they would have landed they saw the ship wherein Sir Perceval had put his sister in.

'Truly,' said Sir Perceval, 'in the name of God, well hath my sister holden us covenant.'

Then took they out of the ship the table of silver, and he took it to Sir Perceval and to Sir Bors to go tofore,[16] and Sir Galahad came behind, and right so they went into the city. And at the gate of the city they saw an old man crooked, and anon Sir Galahad called him and bade him help 'to bear this heavy thing.'

'Truly,' said the old man, 'it is ten year ago that I might not go but with crutches.'

'Care thou not,' said Galahad, 'and arise up and show thy good will!'

And so he essayed, and found himself as whole as ever he was. Then ran he to the table and took one part against [17] Galahad.

Anon arose there a great noise in the city that a cripple was made whole by knights marvellous that entered into the city. Then anon after the three knights went to the water [18] and

---

[15] for the sake of
[16] he took it so that Sir Perceval and Sir Bors should carry the front part (F: *si la prist Boorz et Perceval par devant et Galaad par deriere*)
[17] one side of it next to
[18] sea-shore

brought up into the palace Sir Perceval's sister, and buried her as richly as them ought [19] a king's daughter.

And when the king of that country knew that and saw that fellowship (whose name was Estorause), he asked them of whence they were, and what thing it was that they had brought upon the table of silver. And they told him the truth of the Sankgreall, and the power which God hath set there.

Then this king was a tyrant, and was come of the line of paynims, and took them and put them in prison in a deep hole. But as soon as they were there Our Lord sent them the Sankgreall, through whose grace they were alway fulfilled [20] while that they were in prison.

So at the year's end it befell that this king lay sick and felt that he should die. Then he sent for the three knights, and they came afore him, and he cried them mercy of that he had done to them, and they forgave it him goodly,[1] and he died anon.

When the king was dead all the city stood dismayed and wist not who might be their king. Right so as they were in council there came a voice among them, and bade them choose the youngest knight of three to be their king, 'for he shall well maintain you and all yours.'

So they made Sir Galahad king by all the assent of the whole city, and else they would have slain him. And when he was come to behold his land he let make above the table of silver a chest of gold and of precious stones that covered the holy vessel, and every day early the three knights would come before it and make their prayers.

Now at the year's end, and the self Sunday after that Sir Galahad had borne the crown of gold, he arose up early and his fellows, and came to the palace, and saw tofore them the holy vessel and a man kneeling on his knees in likeness of a bishop that had about him a great fellowship of angels, as it had been Jesu Christ himself. And then he arose and began a mass of Our Lady. And so he came to the sacring, and anon made an end. He called Sir Galahad unto him and said,

'Come forth, the servant of Jesu Christ, and thou shalt see that thou hast much desired to see.'

[19] as it was fitting that they should bury
[20] fed (F: *repeu*)
[1] graciously

And then he began to tremble right hard when the deadly flesh began to behold the spiritual things. Then he held up his hands toward heaven and said,

'Lord, I thank Thee, for now I see that that hath been my desire many a day. Now, my Blessed Lord, I would not live in this wretched world no longer, if it might please Thee, Lord.'

And therewith the good man took Our Lord's Body betwixt his hands, proffered it to Sir Galahad, and he received it right gladly and meekly.

'Now wotest thou what I am?' said the good man.

'Nay, Sir,' said Sir Galahad.

'I am Joseph, the son of Joseph of Arimathea, which Our Lord hath sent to thee to bear thee fellowship. And wotest thou wherefore He hath sent me more than any other? For thou hast resembled me in two things: that thou hast seen, that is the marvels of the Sankgreall, and for thou hast been a clean maiden as I have been and am.'

And when he had said these words Sir Galahad went to Sir Perceval and kissed him and commended him to God. And so he went to Sir Bors and kissed him and commended him to God, and said,

'My fair lord, salew me unto [2] my lord Sir Lancelot, my father, and as soon as ye see him bid him remember of this world unstable.'

And therewith he kneeled down tofore the table and made his prayers. And so suddenly departed his soul to Jesu Christ, and a great multitude of angels bare it up to heaven, even in the sight of his two fellows.

Also these two knights saw come from heaven an hand, but they saw not the body, and so it came right to the vessel, and took it, and the spear, and so bare it up to heaven. And sithen was there never man so hardy to say that he had seen the Sankgreall.

So when Sir Perceval and Sir Bors saw Sir Galahad dead they made as much sorrow as ever did men. And if they had not been good men they might lightly [3] have fallen in despair. And so people of the country and city, they were right heavy. But so he was buried, and as soon as he was buried Sir Perce-

---

[2] greet on my behalf   [3] easily

val yielded him to an hermitage out of the city and took religious clothing. And Sir Bors was alway with him, but he changed never his secular clothing, for that he purposed him to go again into the realm of Logres.

Thus a year and two months lived Sir Perceval in the hermitage a full holy life, and then passed out of the world. Then Sir Bors let bury him by his sister and by Sir Galahad in the spiritualities.[4]

So when Bors saw that he was in so far countries as in the parts of Babylon,[5] he departed from the city of Sarras and armed him and came to the sea, and entered into a ship. And so it befell him, by good adventure, he came unto the realm of Logres, and so he rode a pace[6] till he came to Camelot where the king was.

And then was there made great joy of him in all the court, for they weened all he had been lost forasmuch as he had been so long out of the country. And when they had eaten the king made great clerks to come before him, for cause they should chronicle of[7] the high adventures of the good knights. So when Sir Bors had told him of the high adventures of the Sankgreall such as had befallen him and his three fellows, which were Sir Lancelot, Perceval, Sir Galahad and himself, then Sir Lancelot told the adventures of the Sankgreall that he had seen. All this was made[8] in great books and put up in almeries[9] at Salisbury.

And anon Sir Bors said to Sir Lancelot,

'Sir Galahad, your own son, salewed you by me, and after you my lord King Arthur and all the whole court, and so did Sir Perceval. For I buried them with both mine own hands in the city of Sarras. Also, Sir Lancelot, Sir Galahad prayed you to remember of this unsiker[10] world, as ye behight[11] him when ye were together more than half a year.'

'This is true,' said Sir Lancelot; 'now I trust to God his prayer shall avail me.'

Then Sir Lancelot took Sir Bors in his arms and said,

---

[4] consecrated ground
[5] as remote as the region of Babylon
[6] at a good speed
[7] so that they should place on record

[8] written down
[9] ambries, libraries
[10] unstable, uncertain
[11] promised (*pret. of 'behote'*)

'Cousin, ye are right welcome to me! For all that ever I may do for you and for yours, ye shall find my poor body [12] ready at all times while the spirit is in it, and that I promise you faithfully, and never to fail. And wit ye well, gentle cousin Sir Bors, ye and I shall never depart in sunder [13] while our lives may last.'

'Sir,' said he, 'as ye will, so will I.'

THUS ENDETH THE TALE OF THE SANKGREALL THAT WAS BRIEFLY DRAWN OUT OF FRENCH, WHICH IS A TALE CHRONICLED FOR ONE OF THE TRUEST AND OF THE HOLIEST THAT IS IN THIS WORLD, BY SIR THOMAS MALEORRÉ, KNIGHT.

O BLESSED JESU HELP HIM THROUGH HIS MIGHT! AMEN.

[12] my humble self   [13] never part

The Poisoned Apple

So after the quest of the Sankgreall was fulfilled, and all knights that were left on life were come home again unto the Table Round, as *The Book of the Sankgreall* maketh mention, then was there great joy in the court, and in especial King Arthur and Queen Guinevere made great joy of the remnant that were come home. And passing glad was the king and the queen of Sir Lancelot and of Sir Bors, for they had been passing long away in the quest of the Sankgreall.

Then, as the book saith, Sir Lancelot began to resort unto Queen Guinevere again and forgat the promise and the perfection [1] that he made in the quest; for, as the book saith, had not Sir Lancelot been in his privy thoughts and in his mind so set inwardly to the queen as he was in seeming outward [2] to God, there had no knight passed him in the quest of the Sankgreall. But ever his thoughts privily were on the queen, and so they loved together more hotter than they did toforehand, and had many such privy draughts [3] together that many in the court spake of it, and in especial Sir Agravain, Sir Gawain's brother, for he was ever open-mouthed. [4]

So it befell that Sir Lancelot had many resorts of [5] ladies and damsels which daily resorted unto him, that besought him to be their champion. In all such matters of right Sir Lancelot applied him daily to do for the pleasure of Our Lord Jesu

---

[1] the promise to achieve perfection

[2] to outward appearances

[3] meetings

[4] F: *pour ce qu'il beast* (= '*intended*') *le roi a vengier de sa honte. Paying no attention to the object of the verb 'beer' M took it to mean 'to be wide open, to gape.' Cf. Mod. Fr. 'bouche bée.'*

[5] requests from

Christ, and ever as much as he might he withdrew him from the company of Queen Guinevere for to eschew the slander and noise.[6] Wherefore the queen waxed wroth with Sir Lancelot.

So on a day she called him unto her chamber and said thus:

'Sir Lancelot, I see and feel daily that your love beginneth to slake,[7] for ye have no joy to be in my presence, but ever ye are out of this court, and quarrels and matters [8] ye have nowadays for ladies, maidens and gentlewomen, more than ever ye were wont to have beforehand.'

'Ah, madam,' said Sir Lancelot, 'in this ye must hold me excused for divers causes. One is, I was but late in the quest of the Sankgreall, and I thank God of His great mercy, and never of my deserving,[9] that I saw in that my quest as much as ever saw any sinful man living, and so was it told me. And if that I had not had my privy thoughts to return to your love again as I do, I had [10] seen as great mysteries as ever saw my son, Sir Galahad, Perceval, other Sir Bors. And therefore,[11] madam, I was but late in that quest, and wit you well, madam, it may not be yet lightly [12] forgotten, the high service in whom I did my diligent labour.

'Also, madam, wit you well that there be many men speaketh of our love in this court, and have you and me greatly in await,[13] as this Sir Agravain and Sir Mordred. And, madam, wit you well I dread them more for your sake than for any fear I have of them myself, for I may happen to escape and rid myself [14] in a great need where, madam, ye must abide [15] all that will be said unto you. And then, if that ye fall in any distress throughout [16] wilful [17] folly, then is there none other help but by me and my blood.[18]

'And wit you well, madam, the boldness of you and me will bring us to shame and slander; and that were me loath to see you dishonoured. And that is the cause I take upon me more

6 scandal
7 abate
8 preoccupations
9 though I never deserved it
10 I should have
11 And so
12 easily

13 keep a close watch on you and me
14 I may succeed in escaping and freeing myself
15 face
16 through
17 deliberate
18 kinsmen

for to do for damsels and maidens than ever I did toforn:[19] that men should understand my joy and my delight is my pleasure to have ado for damsels and maidens.'

All this while the queen stood still and let Sir Lancelot say what he would; and when he had all said she brast out of weeping, and so she sobbed and wept a great while. And when she might speak she said,

'Sir Lancelot, now I well understand that thou art a false, recreant knight and a common lecher, and lovest and holdest other ladies, and of me thou hast disdain and scorn. For wit thou well, now I understand thy falsehood I shall never love thee more, and look thou be never so hardy [20] to come in my sight. And right here I discharge [1] thee this court, that thou never come within it, and I forfend thee my fellowship,[2] and upon pain [3] of thy head that thou see me nevermore!'

Right so Sir Lancelot departed with great heaviness,[4] that unneth he might sustain himself [5] for great dole-making.

Then he called Sir Bors, Ector de Maris and Sir Lionel, and told them how the queen had forfended him [6] the court, and so he was in will to depart into his own country.

'Fair sir,' said Bors de Ganis, 'ye shall not depart out of this land by mine advice, for ye must remember you what ye are, and renowned the most noblest knight of the world, and many great matters ye have in hand. And women in their hastiness will do oftentimes that after them sore repenteth. And therefore, by mine advice, ye shall take your horse and ride to the good hermit [7] here beside Windsor, that sometime was a good knight; his name is Sir Brastias. And there shall ye abide till that I send you word of better tidings.'

'Brother,' said Sir Lancelot, 'wit you well I am full loath to depart out of this realm, but the queen hath defended me so highly,[8] that meseemeth she will never be my good lady as she hath been.'

'Say ye never so,' said Sir Bors, 'for many times or this time

[19] hitherto
[20] bold
[1] dismiss
[2] I banish you from my company
[3] at the risk of

[4] sorrow
[5] so great that he could hardly endure
[6] banished him from
[7] M: *ermytayge*
[8] sent me away so angrily

she hath been wroth with you, and after that she was the first that repented it.'

'Ye say well,' said Sir Lancelot, 'for [9] now will I do by your counsel and take mine horse and mine harness and ride to the hermit Sir Brastias, and there will I repose me till I hear some manner of tidings from you. But, fair brother, in that ye can [10] get me the love of my lady, Queen Guinevere.'

'Sir,' said Sir Bors, 'ye need not to move [11] me of such matters, for well ye wot I will do what I may to please you.'

And then Sir Lancelot departed suddenly,[12] and no creature wist where he was become but Sir Bors. So when Sir Lancelot was departed the queen outward made no manner of sorrow in showing to none of his blood [13] nor to none other, but wit ye well, inwardly, as the book saith, she took great thought;[14] but she bare it out with a proud countenance, as though she felt no thought nother danger.[15]

So the queen let make a privy dinner in London unto [16] the knights of the Round Table, and all was for to show outward that she had as great joy in all other knights of the Round Table as she had in Sir Lancelot. So there was all only at that dinner Sir Gawain and his brethren, that is for to say Sir Agravain, Sir Gaheris, Sir Gareth and Sir Mordred, also there was Sir Bors de Ganis, Sir Blamore de Ganis, Sir Bleoberis de Ganis, Sir Galihud, Sir Eliodin, Sir Ector de Maris, Sir Lionel, Sir Palomides, Sir Safir, his brother, Sir La Cote Male Tayle, Sir Persaunt, Sir Ironside, Sir Braundiles, Sir Kay le Seneschal, Sir Mador de la Porte, Sir Patrise, a knight of Ireland, Sir Aliduke, Sir Ascamore, and Sir Pinel le Savage, which was cousin to Sir Lamorak de Galis, the good knight that Sir Gawain and his brethren slew by treason.

And so these four-and-twenty knights should dine with the queen in a privy place by themselves, and there was made a great feast of all manner of dainties. But Sir Gawain had a custom that he used daily at meat and at supper, that [17] he loved well all manner of fruit, and in especial apples and pears.

[9] and
[10] so far as you are able
[11] persuade
[12] quickly
[13] kin.

[14] she was grieved
[15] no sorrow or fear
[16] for
[17] namely

And therefore whosomever dined other feasted Sir Gawain would commonly purvey for [18] good fruit for him. And so did the queen; for to please Sir Gawain she let purvey for [18] him all manner of fruit. For [19] Sir Gawain was a passing hot [20] knight of nature, and this Sir Pinel hated Sir Gawain because of his kinsman Sir Lamorak's death, and therefore, for pure envy [1] and hate, Sir Pinel enpoisoned certain apples for to enpoison Sir Gawain.

So this was well yet unto the end of meat,[2] and so it befell by misfortune a good knight Sir Patrise, which was cousin unto Sir Mador de la Porte, took an apple, for he was enchafed [3] with heat of wine. And it mishapped him to take a poisoned apple. And when he had eaten it he swall sore till he brast,[4] and there Sir Patrise fell down suddenly [5] dead among them.

Then every knight leap from the board ashamed, and araged for [6] wrath out of their wits, for they wist not what to say; considering Queen Guinevere made the feast and dinner they had all suspicion unto her.

'My lady the queen!' said Sir Gawain. 'Madam, wit you that this dinner was made for me and my fellows, for all folks that knoweth my condition understand that I love well fruit. And now I see well I had near been slain. Therefore, madam, I dread me lest ye will be shamed.'

Then the queen stood still and was so sore abashed that she wist not what to say.

'This shall not so be ended,' said Sir Mador de la Porte, 'for here have I lost a full noble knight of my blood,[7] and therefore upon this shame and despite [8] I will be revenged to the utterance!'

And there openly Sir Mador appealed [9] the queen of the death of his cousin Sir Patrise.

Then stood they all still, that [10] none would speak a word against him, for they all had great suspicion unto the queen

---

[18] provide
[19] But
[20] hot-tempered
[1] spite
[2] already near the end of the feast
[3] inflamed

[4] swelled so greatly that he burst
[5] instantly
[6] enraged with
[7] kin
[8] wrong
[9] accused
[10] for

because she let make that dinner. And the queen was so abashed that she could none otherways do but wept so heartily that she fell on a swough. So with this noise and cry came to them King Arthur, and when he wist of the trouble he was a passing heavy man. And ever Sir Mador stood still before the king, and appealed [9] the queen of treason. (For the custom was such at that time that all manner of shameful death [11] was called treason.)

'Fair lords,' said King Arthur, 'me repenteth of this trouble, but the case is so I may not have ado [12] in this matter, for I must be a rightful judge. And that repenteth me that I may not do battle for my wife, for, as I deem, this deed came never by her.[13] And therefore I suppose she shall not be all disdained [14] but that some good knight shall put his body in jeopardy [15] for my queen rather than she should be brent in a wrong quarrel.[16] And therefore, Sir Mador, be not so hasty; for, perdy,[17] it may happen she shall not be all friendless. And therefore desire thou thy day of battle, and she shall purvey her of [18] some good knight that shall answer you, other else it were to me great shame and to all my court.'

'My gracious lord,' said Sir Mador, 'ye must hold me excused, for though ye be our king, in that degree [19] ye are but a knight as we are, and ye are sworn unto knighthood as well as we be.[20] And therefore I beseech you that ye be not displeased, for there is none of all these four-and-twenty knights that were bidden to this dinner but all they have great suspicion unto the queen. What say ye all, my lords?' said Sir Mador.

Then they answered by and by and said they could not excuse the queen for why she made the dinner, and other it must come by her other by her servants.

---

11 murder
12 take action
13 was not her doing
14 utterly dishonoured
15 risk his life
16 unjustly
17 par Dieu
18 provide herself with
19 in (your) rank
20 *In* F. *Mador, in accordance*

with feudal practice, begins by repudiating his allegiance to Arthur ('se devest de toute la terre que il tenoit du roi'). From the point of view of the relationship between king and nobleman as M *sees it there is no need for Mador to do this. The reference to equality of rank is enough to justify his behaviour.*

'Alas,' said the queen, 'I made this dinner for a good intent [1] and never for none evil, so Almighty Jesu help me in my right,[2] as I was never purposed to do such evil deeds, and that I report me unto God.' [3]

'My lord the king,' said Sir Mador, 'I require you as ye be a righteous king, give me my day that [4] I may have justice.'

'Well,' said the king, 'this day fifteen days look thou be ready armed on horseback in the meadow beside Winchester. And if it so fall [5] that there be any knight to encounter against you, there may you do your best, and God speed the right. And if so befall that there be no knight ready at that day, then must my queen be brent, and there she shall be ready to have her judgment.'

'I am answered,' said Sir Mador.

And every knight yode where him liked.

So when the king and the queen were together the king asked the queen how this case [6] befell. Then the queen said,

'Sir, as Jesu be my help!' She wist not how nother in what manner.

'Where is Sir Lancelot?' said King Arthur. 'An he were here he would not grudge to do battle for you.'

'Sir,' said the queen, 'I wot not where he is, but his brother and his kinsmen deem that he be not within this realm.'

'That me repenteth,' said King Arthur, 'for an he were here he would soon stint [7] this strife. Well, then I will counsel you,' said the king, 'that ye go unto Sir Bors, and pray him for to do battle for you for Sir Lancelot's sake, and upon my life he will not refuse you. For well I see,' said the king, 'that none of the four-and-twenty knights that were at your dinner where Sir Patrise was slain that will [8] do battle for you, nother none of them will say well of you, and that shall be great slander to you in this court. But now I miss Sir Lancelot, for an he were here he would soon put me in my heart's ease. What aileth you,' said the king, 'that ye cannot keep Sir Lancelot upon your side? For wit you well,' said the king, 'who that hath Sir Lancelot upon his party [9] hath the

[1] purpose
[2] in my just cause
[3] I trust that God will prove me right
[4] when
[5] happens
[6] misfortune
[7] put an end to
[8] that will = will
[9] side

most man of worship in this world upon his side. Now go your way,' said the king unto the queen, 'and require Sir Bors to do battle for you for Sir Lancelot's sake.'

So the queen departed from the king and sent for Sir Bors into [10] the chamber. And when he came she besought him of succour.

'Madam,' said he, 'what would ye that I did? For I may not with my worship have ado [11] in this matter, because I was at the same dinner, for dread of any of those knights would have you in suspicion. Also, Madam,' said Sir Bors, 'now miss ye Sir Lancelot, for he would not a failed you in your right nother in your wrong, for when ye have been in right great dangers he hath succoured you. And now ye have driven him out of this country, by [12] whom ye and all we were daily worshipped [13] by. Therefore, madam, I marvel how ye dare for shame to [14] require me to do anything for you, insomuch ye have enchased [15] out of your court by whom we were upborne and honoured.' [16]

'Alas, fair knight,' said the queen, 'I put me wholly in your grace, and all that is amiss I will amend as ye will counsel me.' And therewith she kneeled down upon both her knees, and besought Sir Bors to have mercy upon her, 'other else I shall have a shameful death, and thereto I never offended.' [17]

Right so came King Arthur and found the queen kneeling. And then Sir Bors took her up, and said,

'Madam, ye do me great dishonour.'

'Ah, gentle knight,' said the king, 'have mercy upon my queen, courteous knight, for I am now in certain she is untruly defamed! [18] And therefore, courteous knight,' the king said, 'promise her to do battle for her, I require you for the love ye owe unto Sir Lancelot.'

'My lord,' said Sir Bors, 'ye require me the greatest thing that any man may require me. And wit you well, if I grant to do battle for the queen I shall wrath many of my fellowship of the Table Round. But as for that,' said Sir Bors, 'I will grant [19] for my lord Sir Lancelot's sake, and for your sake: I will at

[10] to come into
[11] I cannot honourably take action
[12] through
[13] honoured
[14] how you can decently
[15] driven
[16] the man by whom we were sustained and who brought us honour
[17] and of (all) this I am innocent
[18] slandered
[19] I will agree to do this

that day be the queen's champion unless that there come by
adventures a better knight than I am to do battle for her.'

'Will ye promise me this,' said the king, 'by your faith?'

'Yea sir,' said Sir Bors, 'of that I shall not fail you, nother
her; but if there come a better knight than I am, then shall he
have the battle.'

Then was the king and the queen passing glad, and so
departed, and thanked him heartily.

Then Sir Bors departed secretly upon a day, and rode unto
Sir Lancelot thereas [20] he was with Sir Brastias, and told him
of all this adventure.

'Ah Jesu,' Sir Lancelot said, 'this is come happily as I would
have it. And therefore I pray you make you ready to do
battle, but look that ye tarry till ye see me come as long as
ye may. For I am sure Sir Mador is an hot [1] knight when he
is enchafed,[2] for the more ye suffer [3] him the hastier will he
be to battle.'

'Sir,' said Sir Bors, 'let me deal with him. Doubt ye not ye
shall have all your will.'

So departed Sir Bors from him and came to the court again.
Then it was noised [4] in all the court that Sir Bors should do
battle for the queen, wherefore many knights were displeased
with him that he would take upon him to do battle in the
queen's quarrel; for there were but few knights in all the
court but they deemed the queen was in the wrong and that
she had done that treason. So Sir Bors answered thus to his
fellows of the Table Round.

'Wit you well, my fair lords, it were shame to us all an we
suffered to see [5] the most noble queen of the world to be
shamed openly, considering her lord and our lord is the man
of most worship christened, and he hath ever worshipped [6]
us all in all places.'

Many answered him again:[7] 'As for our most noble King
Arthur, we love him and honour him as well as ye do, but as
for Queen Guinevere we love her not, because she is a
destroyer of good knights.'

'Fair lords,' said Sir Bors, 'meseemeth ye say not as ye

---

[20] to the place where
[1] hot-tempered
[2] roused
[3] keep your distance from

[4] reported
[5] allowed
[6] honoured
[7] made reply

should say, for never yet in my days knew I never ne [8] heard
say that ever she was a destroyer of good knights, but at all
times as far as ever I could know, she was a maintainer [9] of
good knights; and ever she hath been large [10] and free of her
goods to all good knights, and the most bounteous lady of her
gifts and her good grace that ever I saw other heard speak of.
And therefore it were shame to us all and to our most noble
king's wife whom we serve an we suffered her to be shamefully slain. And wit ye well,' said Sir Bors, 'I will not suffer
it, for I dare say so much, for the queen is not guilty of Sir
Patrise's death: for she owed [11] him never none evil will
nother none of the four-and-twenty knights that were at that
dinner, for I dare say for good love she bade us to dinner,
and not for no mal engine.[12] And that, I doubt not, shall be
proved hereafter, for howsomever the game goeth, there was
treason among us.'

Then some said to Bors, 'We may well believe your words.'
And so some were well pleased and some were not.

So the day came on fast until the even that [13] the battle
should be. Then the queen sent for Sir Bors and asked him
how he was disposed.[14]

'Truly, madam,' said he, 'I am disposed [15] in like wise as I
promised you, that is to say I shall not fail you unless there
by adventure come a better knight than I am to do battle for
you. Then, madam, I am of [16] you discharged of [17] my promise.'

'Will ye,' said the queen, 'that I tell my lord the king
thus?'

'Do as it pleaseth you, madam.'

Then the queen yode unto the king and told the answer of
Sir Bors.

'Well, have ye no doubt,' said the king, 'of Sir Bors, for I
call him now that is [18] living one of the noblest knights of the
world, and most perfectest man.'

And thus it passed on till the morn, and so the king and

[8] or
[9] protectress
[10] generous
[11] felt towards
[12] evil intent
[13] the evening before
[14] what his decision was
[15] resolved to act
[16] by
[17] released from
[18] of all that are

the queen and all manner of knights that were there at that
time drew them [19] unto the meadow beside Winchester where
the battle should be. And so when the king was come with
the queen and many knights of the Table Round, so the queen
was then put in the constable's award,[20] and a great fire made
about an iron stake, that an Sir Mador de la Porte had the
better, she should there be brent; for such custom was used
in those days: for favour, love, nother affinity there should
be none other but righteous judgment, as well upon a king as
upon a knight, and as well upon a queen as upon another [1]
poor lady.

So this meanwhile came in Sir Mador de la Porte, and took
his oath before the king, how that the queen did this treason
until [2] his cousin Sir Patrise, 'and unto mine oath I will prove
it with my body, hand for hand, who that will say the con-
trary.'

Right so came in Sir Bors de Ganis and said that as for
Queen Guinevere, 'she is in the right, and that will I make
good that she is not culpable of this treason that is put upon
her.'

'Then make thee ready,' said Sir Mador, 'and we shall prove
whether thou be in the right or I.'

'Sir Mador,' said Sir Bors, 'wit you well, I know you for a
good [3] knight. Notforthen [4] I shall not fear you so greatly
but I trust to God I shall be able to withstand your malice.[5]
But thus much have I promised my lord Arthur and my lady
the queen, that I shall do battle for her in this cause to the
utterest, unless that there come a better knight than I am and
discharge me.'

'Is that all?' asid Sir Mador. 'Other come thou off and do
battle with me, other else say nay!'

'Take your horse,' said Sir Bors, 'and, as I suppose, I shall
not tarry long but ye shall be answered.'

Then either departed to their tents and made them ready to
horseback [6] as they thought best. And anon Sir Mador came
into the field with his shield on his shoulder and his spear in

---

[19] went
[20] custody
[1] any
[2] towards

[3] strong
[4] nevertheless
[5] resist your wickedness
[6] to mount

his hand, and so rode about the place crying unto King
Arthur,

'Bid your champion come forth an he dare!'

Then was Sir Bors ashamed, and took his horse and came to
the lists' end. And then was he ware where came from a
wood there fast by a knight all armed upon a white horse
with a strange shield of strange arms, and he came driving
all that[7] his horse might run. And so he came to Sir Bors
and said thus:

'Fair knight, I pray you be not displeased, for here must a
better knight than ye are have this battle. Therefore I pray
you withdraw you, for wit you well I have had this day a
right great journey and this battle ought to be mine. And so
I promised you when I spake with you last, and with all my
heart I thank you of your good will.'

Then Sir Bors rode unto King Arthur and told him how
there was a knight come that would have the battle to fight
for the queen.

'What knight is he?' said the king.

'I wot not,' said Sir Bors, 'but such covenant he made with
me to be here this day. Now, my lord,' said Sir Bors, 'here
I am discharged.'[8]

Then the king called to that knight, and asked him if he
would fight for the queen. Then he answered and said,

'Sir, therefore come I hither. And therefore, sir king, tarry[9]
me no longer, for anon as I have finished this battle I must
depart hence, for I have to do many battles elsewhere. For
wit you well,' said the knight, 'this is dishonour to you and
to all knights of the Round Table to see and know so noble a
lady and so courteous as Queen Guinevere is, thus to be rebuked[10] and shamed[11] amongst you.'

Then they all marvelled what knight that might be that so
took the battle upon him, for there was not one that knew
him but if it were Sir Bors. Then said Sir Mador de la Porte
unto the king:

'Now let me wit with whom I shall have ado.'

And then they rode to the lists' end, and there they

---

[7] as fast as
[8] released from my obligation
[9] detain

[10] insulted
[11] put to shame

couched [12] their spears and ran together with all their mights.
And anon Sir Mador's spear brake all to pieces, but the other's
spear held and bare Sir Mador's horse and all [13] backwards
to the earth a [14] great fall. But mightily and deliverly [15] he
avoided his horse from him [16] and put his shield before him
and drew his sword and bade the other knight alight and do
battle with him on foot.

Then that knight descended down from his horse and put
his shield before him and drew his sword. And so they came
eagerly unto battle, and either gave other many sad strokes,
tracing and traversing and foining together [17] with their
swords as it were wild boars, thus fighting nigh an hour; for
this Sir Mador was a strong knight, and mightily proved in
many strong [18] battles. But at the last this knight smote Sir
Mador grovelling upon the earth, and the knight stepped
near him to have pulled Sir Mador flatling [19] upon the ground;
and therewith Sir Mador arose, and in his rising he smote
that knight through the thick of the thighs, that the blood
brast out fiercely.

And when he felt himself so wounded and saw his blood,
he let him arise upon his feet, and then he gave him such a
buffet upon the helm that he fell to the earth flatling.[19] And
therewith he strode to him to have pulled off his helm off his
head. And so Sir Mador prayed that knight to save his life.
And so he yielded him as overcome, and released the queen
of his quarrel.[20]

'I will not grant thee thy life,' said the knight, 'only that
thou freely release [1] the queen forever, and that no mention
be made upon Sir Patrise's tomb that ever Queen Guinevere
consented to that treason.'

'All this shall be done,' said Sir Mador, 'I clearly discharge
my quarrel [2] forever.'

Then the knights parters [3] of the lists took up Sir Mador
and led him till his tent. And the other knight went straight

---

[12] lowered
[13] and the rider
[14] in a
[15] speedily
[16] freed himself from his horse
[17] moving from side to side and
thrusting at each other

[18] arduous
[19] at full length
[20] accusation
[1] fully exonerate
[2] withdraw my accusation
[3] stewards

to the stairfoot where sat King Arthur. And by that time was
the queen came to the king, and either kissed other heartily.

And when the king saw that knight he stooped down to
him and thanked him, and in like wise did the queen. And
the king prayed him put off his helmet and to repose him and
to take a sop of wine.

And then he put off his helm to drink, and then every
knight knew him that it was Sir Lancelot. And anon as the
king wist that, he took the queen in his hand and yode unto
Sir Lancelot and said,

'Sir, gramercy of your great travail [4] that ye have had this
day for me and for my queen.'

'My lord,' said Sir Lancelot, 'wit you well I ought of right
ever to be in your quarrel, and in my lady the queen's
quarrel,[5] to do battle; for ye are the man that gave me the
high Order of Knighthood, and that day my lady, your
queen, did me worship.[6] And else I had been shamed, for
that same day that ye made me knight through my hastiness [7]
I lost my sword, and my lady, your queen, found it, and
lapped [8] it in her train, and gave me my sword when I had
need thereto; and else had I been shamed among all knights.
And therefore, my lord Arthur, I promised her at that day
ever to be her knight in right other in wrong.' [9]

'Gramercy,' said the king, 'for this journey. And wit you
well,' said the king, 'I shall acquit [10] your goodness.'

And evermore the queen beheld Sir Lancelot and wept so
tenderly that she sank almost to the ground for sorrow, that [11]
he had done to her so great kindness where she showed him
great unkindness. Then the knights of his blood drew unto
him, and there either of them made great joy of other. And
so came all the knights of the Table Round that were there
at that time and welcomed him.

---

4 labour
5 on your side and on my lady
the queen's side
6 honour
7 haste, rashness
8 wrapped
9 *This explanation of Lancelot's
allegiance to Guinevere occurs in
the Prose Lancelot (ed. Sommer,
III, 127–37), but not in F. As
Lancelot was being knighted news
was brought of an important adventure, and Arthur forgot to give
him his sword. The investiture
was completed when Guinevere,
on receiving homage from Lancelot's defeated opponent, sent her
young champion a beautiful sword
'richement appareillie de fuerre et
de renge.'*
10 reward, repay
11 because

And then Sir Mador was healed of [12] his leechcraft, and Sir Lancelot was healed of his play.[13] And so there was made great joy and many mirths there was made in that court.

And so it befell that the Damsel of the Lake that hight Ninive, which wedded the good knight Sir Pelleas, and so she came to the court, for ever she did great goodness unto King Arthur and to all his knights through her sorcery and enchantments. And so when she heard how the queen was grieved for the death of Sir Patrise, then she told it openly that she was never guilty, and there she disclosed by whom it was done, and named him Sir Pinel, and for what cause he did it. There it was openly known and disclosed, and so the queen was excused.[14] And this knight Sir Pinel fled into his country, and was openly known that he enpoisoned the apples at that feast to that intent to have destroyed Sir Gawain, because Sir Gawain and his brethren destroyed Sir Lamorak de Galis which Sir Pinel was cousin unto.

Then was Sir Patrise buried in the church of Westminster in a tomb, and thereupon was written: 'Here lieth Sir Patrise of Ireland, slain by Sir Pinel le Savage, that enpoisoned apples to have slain Sir Gawain, and by misfortune Sir Patrise ate one of the apples, and then suddenly [15] he brast.' Also there was written upon the tomb that Queen Guinevere was appealed of treason of the death [16] of Sir Patrise by Sir Mador de la Porte, and there was made the mention how Sir Lancelot fought with him for Queen Guinevere and overcame him in plain battle. All this was written upon the tomb of Sir Patrise in excusing of the queen.

And then Sir Mador sued daily and long to have the queen's good grace, and so by the means of Sir Lancelot he [17] caused him to stand in the queen's good grace, and all was forgiven.

---

[12] by
[13] wound (F: *plaie*)
[14] *In F, Guinevere is 'excused' solely as a result of Lancelot's victory, and there is no reference to the Damsel of the Lake's disclosures. M must have thought that the evidence of a judicial combat was not enough.*
[15] instantly
[16] accused of treacherously causing the death
[17] i.e. Lancelot

The Fair Maid of Astolat

Thus it passed until Our Lady Day of the Assumption. Within a fifteen days of that feast the king let cry a great jousts and a tournament that should be at that day at Camelot, otherwise called Winchester.[1] And the king let cry[2] that he and the king of Scots would joust against all the world.

And when this cry was made, thither came many good knights, that is to say the King of North Wales, and King Anguish of Ireland, and the King with the Hundred Knights, and Sir Galahalt the Haut Prince, and the King of Northumberland, and many other noble dukes and earls of others divers countries.

So King Arthur made him ready to depart to his jousts, and would have had the queen with him; but at that time she would not, she said, for she was sick and might not ride.

'That me repenteth,' said the king, 'for this seven year ye saw not such a noble fellowship together except at the Whitsuntide when Sir Galahad departed from the court.'

'Truly,' said the queen, 'ye must hold me excused, I may not be there.'

And many deemed the queen would not be there because of Sir Lancelot, for he would not ride with the king, for he said he was not whole of the play[3] of Sir Mador. Wherefore the king was heavy[4] and passing wroth, and so he departed toward Winchester with his fellowship.

And so by the way the king lodged at a town called Astolat,

[1] *No such identification is suggested in* F. *Caxton in his Preface to* Le Morte Darthur *describes Camelot as a city in Wales.*

[2] let it be proclaimed
[3] wound (F: *plaie*)
[4] grieved

133

that is in English Guildford,[5] and there the king lay in the castle. So when the king was departed the queen called Sir Lancelot unto her and said thus:

'Sir, ye are greatly to blame thus to hold you [6] behind my lord. What will your enemies and mine say and deem? "See how Sir Lancelot holdeth him ever behind the king, and so the queen doth also, for that they would [7] have their pleasure together." And thus will they say,' said the queen.

'Have ye no doubt, madam,' said Sir Lancelot. 'I allow your wit.[8] It is of late come syn ye were waxen [9] so wise! And therefore, madam, at this time I will be ruled by your counsel, and this night I will take my rest, and to-morrow betime I will take my way toward Winchester. But wit you well,' said Sir Lancelot unto the queen, 'at that jousts I will be against the king and against all his fellowship.'

'Sir, ye may there do as ye list,' said the queen, 'but by my counsel ye shall not be against your king and your fellowship, for there been full many hardy [10] knights of your blood.'

'Madam,' said Sir Lancelot, 'I shall take the adventure that God will give me.'

And so upon the morn early he heard mass and dined, and so he took his leave of the queen and departed. And then he rode so much unto the time [11] he came to Astolat; and there it happened him that in the evening-tide he came to an old baron's place that hight Sir Barnard of Astolat. And as Sir Lancelot entered into his lodging, King Arthur espied him as he did walk in a garden beside the castle: he knew him well enough.

'Well, sirs,' said King Arthur unto his knights that were by him beside the castle, 'I have now espied one knight,' he said, 'that will play his play [12] at the jousts, I undertake.'

'Who is that?' said the knights.

'At this time ye shall not wit for me,' said the king, and smiled, and went to his lodging.

---

[5] *A natural halt on the way from London to Winchester. By Malory's time the residential quarters of Guildford castle were in ruins and therefore fit to be associated with Arthur's reign.*

[6] remain

[7] because they wish to

[8] I commend your judgment

[9] It is not long since you have grown

[10] brave

[11] until

[12] perform valiant deeds

So when Sir Lancelot was in his lodging, and unarmed in his chamber, the old baron, Sir Barnard, came to him and welcomed him in the best manner, but he knew not Sir Lancelot.

'Fair sir,' said Sir Lancelot till [13] his host, 'I would pray you to lend me a shield that were not openly known, for mine is well known.'

'Sir,' said his host, 'ye shall have your desire, for meseemth ye be one of the likeliest [14] knights that ever I saw, and therefore, sir, I shall show you friendship.' And said: 'Sir, wit you well I have two sons that were but late made knights. And the eldest hight Sir Tirry, and he was hurt that same day he was made knight, and he may not ride; and his shield ye shall have, for that is not known, I daresay, but here and in no place else.' And his younger son hight Sir Lavain. 'And if it please you, he shall ride with you unto that jousts, for he is of [15] his age strong and wight.[16] For much my heart giveth unto [17] you, that [18] ye should be a noble knight. And therefore I pray you to tell me your name,' said Sir Barnard.

'As for that,' said Sir Lancelot, 'ye must hold me excused as at this time. And if God give me grace to speed well at the jousts I shall come again and tell you my name. But I pray you in any wise let me have your son, Sir Lavain, with me, and that I may have his brother's shield.'

'Sir, all this shall be done,' said Sir Barnard.

So this old baron had a daughter that was called that time the Fair Maiden of Astolat, and ever she beheld Sir Lancelot wonderfully.[19] And as the book saith, she cast such a love unto [20] Sir Lancelot that she could never withdraw her love, wherefore she died. And her name was Elaine le Blanke.

So thus as she came to and fro she was so hot in love that she besought Sir Lancelot to wear upon him at the jousts a token of hers.

'Damsel,' said Sir Lancelot, 'and if I grant you that, ye may say that I do more for your love [1] than ever I did for lady or gentlewoman.'

Then he remembered himself that he would go to the jousts

[13] to	[18] because
[14] handsomest	[19] with admiration
[15] for	[20] had so great a love for
[16] stalwart	[1] for your sake
[17] I feel drawn to you	

disguised, and because he had never aforn [2] borne no manner
of token of no [3] damsel, he bethought him to bear a token of
hers, that [4] none of his blood thereby might know him.[5] And
then he said,

'Fair maiden, I will grant you to wear a token of yours
upon mine helmet. And therefore what is it? Show ye it me.'

'Sir,' she said, 'it is a red sleeve of mine, of scarlet, well
embroidered with great pearls.'

And so she brought it him. So Sir Lancelot received it and
said,

'Never did I erst [6] so much for no damsel.'

Then Sir Lancelot betook [7] the fair maiden his shield in
keeping, and prayed her to keep it until time that he come
again.[8] And so that night he had merry rest and great cheer,
for this damsel Elaine was ever about Sir Lancelot all the
while she might be suffered.[9]

So upon a day, on the morn, King Arthur and all his
knights departed, for there the king had tarried three days to
abide his noble knights. And so when the king was ridden,
Sir Lancelot and Sir Lavain made them ready to ride, and
either of them had white shields, and the red sleeve Sir
Lancelot let carry with him.

And so they took their leave at Sir Barnard, the old baron,
and at his daughter, the fair maiden, and then they rode so
long till they came to Camelot, that time called Winchester.
And there was great press [10] of kings, dukes, earls and barons,
and many noble knights. But Sir Lancelot was lodged privily
by the means of Sir Lavain with a rich burgess, that no man
in that town was ware what they were. And so they reposed
them there till Our Lady Day of the Assumption, that [11] the
great jousts should be.

So when trumpets blew unto the field, and King Arthur

---

[2] before
[3] for any
[4] so that
[5] *In* F *the damsel asks Lancelot
a boon in the name of his lady
('par la foi que tu doiz a la riens
el monde que tu mieuz ainmes')
and Lancelot cannot refuse it
without infringing the code of*
*courtly love ('car trop m'avés
conjuré'). M supplies him with a
simpler motive.*
[6] hitherto
[7] entrusted to
[8] until he returned
[9] allowed
[10] throng
[11] when

was set on high upon a chafflet [12] to behold who did best (but, as the French book saith, the king would not suffer Sir Gawain to go from him, for never had Sir Gawain the better an Sir Lancelot were in the field, and many times was Sir Gawain rebuked so when Sir Lancelot was in the field in any jousts disguised), then some of the kings, as King Anguish of Ireland and the King of Scots, were that time turned [13] to be upon the side of King Arthur. And then the other party was the King of North Wales, and the King with the Hundred Knights, and the King of Northumberland, and Sir Galahalt the Haut Prince. But these three kings and this duke was passing [14] weak to hold against Arthur's party, for with him [15] were the noblest knights of the world.

So then they withdrew them either party from other and every man made him ready in his best manner to do what he might. Then Sir Lancelot made him ready and put the red sleeve upon his helmet and fastened it fast. And so Sir Lancelot and Sir Lavain departed out of Winchester privily and rode until [16] a little leaved [17] wood behind the party that held against King Arthur party. And there they held them [18] still till the parties smote together. And then came in the King of Scots and the King of Ireland on King Arthur's party, and against them came in the King of Northumberland and the King with the Hundred Knights.

And there began a great medley, and there the King of Scots smote down the King of Northumberland, and the King with the Hundred Knights smote down King Anguish of Ireland. Then Sir Palomides, that was on Arthur's party, he encountered with Sir Galahalt, and either of them smote down other, and either party helped their lords on horseback again. So there began a strong assail [19] on both parties.

And then came in Sir Braundiles, Sir Sagramore le Desirous, Sir Dodinas le Savage, Sir Kay le Seneschal, Sir Grifflet le Fyz de Dieu, Sir Lucan de Butler, Sir Bedivere, Sir Agravain, Sir Gaheris, Sir Mordred, Sir Meliot de Logres, Sir Ozanna le Cure Hardy, Sir Safir, Sir Epinogris, Sir Galleron of Galway.

[12] platform
[13] decided
[14] too
[15] with Arthur
[16] to
[17] leafy
[18] remained
[19] attack

All these fifteen knights, that were knights of the Round
Table, so these with more other came in together and beat
aback the King of Northumberland and the King of North
Wales.

When Sir Lancelot saw this, as he hoved [20] in the little
leaved [17] wood, then he said unto Sir Lavain,

'See yonder is a company of good knights, and they hold
them [1] together as boars that were chased with dogs.'

'That is truth,' said Sir Lavain.

'Now,' said Sir Lancelot, 'an ye will help a little, ye shall
see the yonder fellowship that chaseth now these men on
our side, that they shall go as fast backward as they went
forward.'

'Sir, spare ye not for my part,' [2] said Sir Lavain, 'for I shall
do what I may.'

Then Sir Lancelot and Sir Lavain came in at the thickest
of the press, and there Sir Lancelot smote down Sir Braundiles, Sir Sagramore, Sir Dodinas, Sir Kay, Sir Grifflet, and all
this he did with one spear. And Sir Lavain smote down Sir
Lucan de Butler and Sir Bedivere. And then Sir Lancelot gat
another great spear, and there he smote down Sir Agravain
and Sir Gaheris, Sir Mordred, Sir Meliot de Logres; and Sir
Lavain smote down Sir Ozanna le Cure Hardy. And then
Sir Lancelot drew his sword, and there he smote on the right
hand and on the left hand, and by great force he unhorsed
Sir Safir, Sir Epinogris, and Sir Galleron.

And then the knights of the Table Round withdrew them
aback, after they had gotten their horses as well as they might.

'Ah, mercy Jesu,' said Sir Gawain. 'What knight is yonder
that doth so marvellous deeds in that field?'

'I wot what he is,' said the king, 'but as at this time I will
not name him.'

'Sir,' said Sir Gawain, 'I would say it were Sir Lancelot by
his riding and his buffets [3] that I see him deal. But ever
meseemeth it should not be he, for that he beareth the red
sleeve upon his helmet; for I wist him never bear token at
no jousts of lady ne gentlewoman.'

[20] stood
[1] keep
[2] do not hold back on my account
[3] blows

'Let him be,' said King Arthur, 'for he will be better known and do more or ever he depart.'

Then the party that was against King Arthur were well comforted, and then they held them [4] together that beforehand were sore rebuked.[5] Then Sir Bors, Sir Ector de Maris, and Sir Lionel, they called unto them the knights of their blood, as Sir Blamore de Ganis, Sir Bleoberis, Sir Aliduke, Sir Galihud, Sir Eliodin, Sir Bellengere le Beuse. So these nine knights of Sir Lancelot's kin thrust in mightily, for they were all noble knights, and they of great hate and despite [6] thought to rebuke [7] Sir Lancelot and Sir Lavain, for they knew them not.

And so they came hurling together and smote down many knights of North Wales and of Northumberland. And when Sir Lancelot saw them fare so, he gat a great spear in his hand; and there encountered with him all at once, Sir Bors, Sir Ector, and Sir Lionel. And they three smote him at once with their spears, and with force of themself [8] they smote Sir Lancelot's horse revers [9] to the earth. And by misfortune Sir Bors smote Sir Lancelot through the shield into the side, and the spear brake, and the head left still [10] in the side.

When Sir Lavain saw his master lie on the ground he ran to the King of Scots and smote him to the earth; and by great force he took his horse and brought him to Sir Lancelot, and maugre [11] them all he made him to mount upon that horse. And then Sir Lancelot gat a spear in his hand, and there he smote Sir Bors, horse and man, to the earth; and in the same wise he served Sir Ector and Sir Lionel; and Sir Lavain smote down Sir Blamore de Ganis. And then Sir Lancelot drew his sword, for he felt himself so sore hurt that he weened there to have had his death. And then he smote Sir Bleoberis such a buffet on the helmet that he fell down to the earth in a swoon and in the same wise he served Sir Aliduke and Sir Galihud. And Sir Lavain smote down Sir Bellengere that was son to Alisaunder le Orphelin.

And by [12] this was done was Sir Bors horsed again and in

[4] pressed the attack
[5] shamefully defeated
[6] angered and resentful
[7] defeat
[8] with their combined strength
[9] with back-handed blows
[10] sticking
[11] in spite of
[12] when

came with Sir Ector and Sir Lionel, and all they three smote
with their swords upon Sir Lancelot's helmet. And when he felt
their buffets, and with that [13] his wound grieved him grievously, then he thought to do what he might while he could
endure. And then he gave Sir Bors such a buffet that he made
him bow his head passing low; and therewithal he raced off [14]
his helm, and might have slain him, but when he saw his visage
so pulled him down. And in the same wise he served Sir Ector
and Sir Lionel; for, as the book saith, he might have slain them,
but when he saw their visages his heart might not serve him
thereto,[15] but left them there.

And then afterwards he hurled into the thickest press [16] of
them all, and did there the marvelloust [17] deeds of arms that
ever man saw, and ever Sir Lavain with him. And there Sir
Lancelot with his sword smote down and pulled down, as the
French book saith, more than thirty knights, and the most
party were [18] of the Table Round. And there Sir Lavain did
full well that day, for he smote down ten knights of the Table
Round.

'Mercy, Jesu,' said Sir Gawain unto King Arthur, 'I marvel
what knight that he is with the red sleeve.'

'Sir,' said King Arthur, 'he will be known or ever he depart.'

And then the king blew unto lodging,[19] and the prize was
given by heralds unto the knight with the white shield that
bare the red sleeve. Then came the King of North Wales, and
the King of Northumberland, and the King with the Hundred
Knights, and Sir Galahalt the Haut Prince, and said unto Sir
Lancelot:

'Fair knight, God you bless, for much have ye done for us
this day. And therefore we pray you that ye will come with
us, that ye may receive the honour and the prize as ye have
worshipfully [20] deserved it.'

'Fair lords,' said Sir Lancelot, 'wit ye well, if I have deserved thank I have sore [1] bought it, and that me repenteth it,
for I am never like [2] to escape with the life. Therefore, my

[13] and as
[14] tore off
[15] had no heart to do it
[16] throng
[17] most wonderful
[18] they were mostly
[19] ordered that the fighting should cease for the night
[20] honourably
[1] dearly
[2] unlikely

fair lords, I pray you that ye will suffer me to depart where me liketh, for I am sore hurt. And I take none force of none [3] honour, for I had liefer repose me [4] than to be lord of all the world.'

And therewithal he groaned piteously, and rode a great wallop [5] awayward from them until he came under a wood's eves.[6] And when he saw that he was from the field nigh a mile, that he was sure he might not be seen, then he said with an high voice and with a great groan,

'Ah, gentle knight, Sir Lavain! help me that this truncheon [7] were out of my side, for it sticketh so sore that it nigh slayeth me.'

'Ah, mine own lord,' said Sir Lavain, 'I would fain do that might please you, but I dread me sore, an I pull out the truncheon,[7] that ye shall be in peril of death.'

'I charge[8] you,' said Sir Lancelot, 'as ye love me, draw it out!'

And therewithal he descended from his horse, and right so did Sir Lavain; and forthwithal he drew the truncheon [7] out of his side, and gave a great shriek and a grisly groan that [9] the blood brast out nigh a pint at once, that at the last [10] he sank down upon his arse and so swooned down, pale and deadly.

'Alas,' said Sir Lavain, 'what shall I do?'

And then he turned Sir Lancelot into the wind, and so he lay there nigh half-an-hour as he had been dead. And so at the last Sir Lancelot cast up his eyen, and said,

'Ah, Sir Lavain, help me that I were on my horse! For here is fast by, within this two mile, a gentle [11] hermit that sometime was a full noble knight and a gread lord of possessions. And for great goodness he hath taken him to wilful [12] poverty, and forsaken mighty lands. And his name is Sir Baudwin of Britain, and he is a full noble surgeon and a good leech. Now let see and help me up that I were there, for ever my heart giveth me [13] that I shall never die of my cousin-germain's [14] hands.'

---

[3] I do not care for any
[4] I would sooner rest
[5] gallop
[6] the edge of a wood
[7] shaft (of spear)
[8] command
[9] as
[10] and presently
[11] noble
[12] voluntary
[13] tells me
[14] first cousin's

And then with great pain Sir Lavain holp him upon his
horse, and then they rode a great wallop [15] together, and ever
Sir Lancelot bled, that it [16] ran down to the earth. And so by
fortune they came to an hermitage which was under a wood,
and a great cliff on the other side, and a fair water [17] running
under it. And then Sir Lavain beat on the gate with the butt
of his spear and cried fast,[18]

'Let in, for Jesu's sake!'

And anon there came a fair child [19] to them and asked them
what they would.

'Fair son,' said Sir Lavain, 'go and pray thy lord the hermit
for God's sake to let in here a knight that is full sore wounded.
And this day, tell thy lord, I saw him do more deeds of arms
than ever I heard say that any man did.'

So the child went in lightly,[20] and then he brought the
hermit which was a passing likely [1] man. When Sir Lavain
saw him he prayed him for God's sake of succour.

'What knight is he?' said the hermit. 'Is he of the house of
King Arthur or not?'

'I wot not,' said Sir Lavain, 'what he is, nother what is his
name, but well I wot I saw him do marvellously this day as of
deeds of arms.'

'On whose party was he?' said the hermit.

'Sir,' said Sir Lavain, 'he was this day against King Arthur,
and there he won the prize of all the knights of the Round
Table.'

'I have seen the day,' said the hermit, 'I would have loved
him the worse because he was against my lord, King Arthur,
for sometime I was one of the fellowship, but now I thank
God I am otherwise disposed. But where is he? Let me see
him.'

Then Sir Lavain brought the hermit to him. And when the
hermit beheld him as he sat leaning upon his saddle-bow, ever
bleeding spiteously,[2] and ever the knight hermit thought that
he should know him; but he could not bring him to knowledge
because he was so pale for bleeding.

---

[15] at full speed
[16] so that the blood
[17] stream
[18] loudly

[19] handsome young nobleman
[20] quickly
[1] handsome
[2] copiously

'What knight are ye,' said the hermit, 'and where were ye born?'

'My fair lord,' said Sir Lancelot, 'I am a stranger and a knight adventurous that laboureth throughout many ·realms for to win worship.'

Then the hermit advised him better [3] and saw by a wound on his cheek that he was Sir Lancelot.

'Alas,' said the hermit, 'mine own lord! Why lain [4] you your name from me? Perdy,[5] I ought to know you of right, for ye are the most noblest knight of the world. For well I know you for Sir Lancelot.'

'Sir,' said he, 'sith ye know me, help me, an ye may, for God's sake! For I would be out of this pain at once, other to death other to life.'

'Have ye no doubt,' said the hermit, 'for ye shall live and fare right well.'

And so the hermit called to him two of his servants, and so they bare him into the hermitage, and lightly unarmed him, and laid him in his bed. And then anon the hermit staunched his blood and made him to drink good wine, that he was well revigoured and knew himself.[6] For in these days it was not the guise [7] as is nowadays; for there were none hermits in those days but that they had been men of worship and of prowess, and those hermits held great households and refreshed [8] people that were in distress.

Now turn we unto King Arthur, and leave Sir Lancelot in the hermitage. So when the kings were together on both parties, and the great feast should be holden, King Arthur asked the King of North Wales and their fellowship where was that knight that bare the red sleeve.

'Let bring him before me, that he may have his laud and honour and the prize,[9] as it is right.'

Then spake Sir Galahalt the Haut Prince and the King with the Hundred Knights, and said,

'We suppose that knight is mischieved [10] so that he is never

---

[3] thought again
[4] conceal
[5] par Dieu
[6] so that his strength returned and his spirits revived
[7] custom
[8] succoured
[9] be praised, honoured and rewarded
[10] come to some harm

like to see you nother none of us all. And that is the greatest pity that ever we wist of any knight.'

'Alas,' said King Arthur, 'how may this be? Is he so sore hurt? But what is his name?' said King Arthur.

'Truly,' said they all, 'we know not his name, nother from whence he came, nother whither he would.'

'Alas,' said the king, 'this is the worst tidings that came to me this seven year! For I would not for all the lands I wield to know and wit it were so that that noble knight were slain.'

'Sir, know ye aught of him?' said they all.

'As for that,' said King Arthur, 'whether I know him other none, ye shall not know for me what man he is but [11] Almighty Jesu send me good tidings of him.'

And so said they all.

'By my head,' said Sir Gawain, 'if it so be that the good knight be so sore hurt, it is great damage [12] and pity to all this land, for he is one of the noblest knights that ever I saw in a field handle spear or sword. And if he may be found I shall find him, for I am sure he is not far from this country.'

'Sir, ye bear you well,' said King Arthur, 'and ye may find him, unless that he be in such a plight that he may not wield himself.' [13]

'Jesu defend!' said Sir Gawain. 'But wit well I shall know what he is an I may find him.'

Right so Sir Gawain took a squire with him upon hackneys [14] and rode all about Camelot within six or seven mile, but soon [15] he came again [16] and could hear no word of him. Then within two days King Arthur and all the fellowship returned unto London again. And so as they rode by the way it happened Sir Gawain at Astolat to lodge with Sir Barnard thereas [17] was Sir Lancelot lodged.

And so as Sir Gawain was in his chamber to repose him Sir Barnard, the old baron, came in to him, and his daughter Elaine, to cheer him and to ask him what tidings, and who did best at the tournament of Winchester.

'So God me help,' said Sir Gawain, 'there were two knights

---

[11] until
[12] a misfortune
[13] has lost consciousness (*cf. O, p. 394, l. 16*)
[14] hacks
[15] M: *so*
[16] back
[17] where

that bare white shields, but one of them bare a red sleeve upon his head, and certainly he was the best knight that ever I saw joust in field. For I dare say,' said Sir Gawain, 'that one knight with the red sleeve smote down forty knights of the Round Table, and his fellow did right well and worshipfully.'

'Now blessed be God,' said this fair maiden of Astolat, 'that that knight sped so well! For he is the man in the world that I first loved,[18] and truly he shall be the last that ever I shall love.'

'Now, fair maiden,' said Sir Gawain, 'is that good knight your love?' [19]

'Certainly, sir,' said she, 'he is my love.' [20]

'Then know ye his name?' said Sir Gawain.

'Nay truly, sir,' said the damsel, 'I know not his name nother from whence he came, but to say that I love him, I promise God and you I love him.'

'How had ye knowledge of him first?' said Sir Gawain.

Then she told him, as ye have heard before, and how her father betook [1] him her brother to do him service, and how her father lent him her brother's, Sir Tirry's, shield: 'and here with me he left his own shield.'

'For what cause did he so?' said Sir Gawain.

'For this cause,' said the damsel, 'for his shield was full well known among many noble knights.'

'Ah, fair damsel,' said Sir Gawain, 'please it you let me have a sight of that shield?'

'Sir,' she said, 'it is in my chamber, covered with a case, and if ye will come with me ye shall see it.'

'Not so,' said Sir Barnard to his daughter, 'but send ye for that shield.'

So when the shield was come,[2] Sir Gawain took off the case, and when he beheld that shield he knew it anon that it was Sir Lancelot's shield and his own arms.

'Ah, Jesu, mercy!' said Sir Gawain, 'now is my heart more heavier than ever it was tofore.'

'Why?' said this maid Elaine.

'For I have a great cause,' said Sir Gawain. 'Is that knight that oweth this shield [3] your love?' [19]

---

[18] that was my first love	[1] entrusted to
[19] lover *or* beloved	[2] brought
[20] beloved	[3] to whom this shield belongs

'Yea, truly,' she said, 'my love [4] is he. God would that I were his love.' [4]

'So God me speed,' said Sir Gawain, 'fair damsel, ye have right,[5] for an he be your love [4] ye love the most honourablest knight of the world and the man of most worship.'

'So methought ever,' said the damsel, 'for never or that time no knight that ever I saw loved I never none erst.' [6]

'God grant,' said Sir Gawain, 'that either of you may rejoice other, but that is in a great adventure.[7] But truly,' said Sir Gawain unto the damsel, 'ye may say ye have a fair grace,[8] for why I have known that noble knight this four-and-twenty year, and never or that day I nor none other knight, I dare make good, saw never nother heard say that ever he bare token or sign of no lady, gentlewoman, nor maiden at no jousts nother tournament.[9] And therefore, fair maiden, ye are much beholden to him to give him thank. But I dread me,' said Sir Gawain, 'that ye shall never see him in this world, and that is as great pity as ever was of any earthly man.'

'Alas!' said she, 'how may this be? Is he slain?'

'I say not so,' said Sir Gawain, 'but wit you well he is grievously wounded, by all manner of signs, and by means of sight [10] more likelier to be dead than to be on live. And wit you well he is the noble knight Sir Lancelot, for by this shield I know him.'

'Alas!' said this fair maiden of Astolat, 'how may this be? And what was his hurt?'

'Truly,' said Sir Gawain, 'the man in the world that loved best him hurt him. And I dare say,' said Sir Gawain, 'an that knight that hurt him knew the very certainty [11] that he had hurt Sir Lancelot, it were the most sorrow that ever came to his heart.'

'Now, fair father,' said then Elaine, 'I require you give me leave to ride and seek him, other else I wot well I shall go out of my mind. For I shall never stint till that I find him and my brother, Sir Lavain.'

---

[4] beloved
[5] are right
[6] for never before did I see any knight that I loved
[7] there is little chance of this
[8] you are extremely fortunate
[9] never before that day did I or any other knight . . . see or hear say that he ever carried a token at a tournament
[10] by his looks
[11] for certain

'Do ye as it liketh you,' said her father, 'for me sore repenteth of the hurt of that noble knight.'

Right so the maid made her ready and departed before Sir Gawain making great dole. Then on the morn Sir Gawain came to King Arthur and told him all how he had found Sir Lancelot's shield in the keeping of the fair maiden of Astolat.

'All that knew I aforehand,' said King Arthur, 'and that caused me I would not suffer [12] you to have ado [13] at the great jousts; for I espied him when he came until [14] his lodging, full late in the evening, into Astolat. But great marvel have I,' said King Arthur, 'that ever he would bear any sign of any damsel, for or now I never heard say nor knew that ever he bare any token of none earthly woman.'

'By my head, sir,' said Sir Gawain, 'the fair maiden of Astolat loveth him marvellously well. What it meaneth I cannot say. And she is ridden after to seek him.'

So the king and all came to London, and there Gawain all openly disclosed it to all the court that it was Sir Lancelot that jousted best. And when Sir Bors heard that, wit you well he was an heavy [15] man, and so were all his kinsmen. But when the queen wist that it was Sir Lancelot that bare the red sleeve of the fair maiden of Astolat, she was nigh out of her mind for wrath. And then she sent for Sir Bors de Ganis in all haste that might be. So when Sir Bors was come before the queen she said,

'Ah, Sir Bors! Have ye not heard say how falsely Sir Lancelot hath betrayed me?'

'Alas, madam,' said Sir Bors, 'I am afeard he hath betrayed himself and us all.'

'No force,' [16] said the queen, 'though he be destroyed, for he is a false traitor-knight.'

'Madam,' said Sir Bors, 'I pray you say ye no more so, for wit you well I may not hear no such language of him.'

'Why so, Sir Bors?' said she. 'Should I not call him traitor when he bare the red sleeve upon his head at Winchester, at the great jousts?'

'Madam,' said Sir Bors, 'that sleeve-bearing repenteth me,[17]

[12] allow
[13] to fight
[14] to

[15] sorrowful
[16] No matter
[17] I regret

but I dare say he did bear it to none [18] evil intent, but for this cause he bare the red sleeve that none of his blood [19] should know him. For or then we nother none of us all never knew that ever he bare token or sign of maiden, lady, nother gentlewoman.'

'Fie on him!' said the queen. 'Yet for all his pride and bobaunce,[20] there ye proved yourself better man than he.'

'Nay, madam, say ye nevermore so, for he beat me and my fellows, and might have slain us an he had would.'

'Fie on him!' said the queen. 'For I heard Sir Gawain say before my lord Arthur that it were marvel to tell the great love that is between the fair maiden of Astolat and him.'

'Madam,' said Sir Bors, 'I may not warn [1] Sir Gawain to say what it pleaseth him, but I daresay, as for my lord Sir Lancelot, that he loveth no lady, gentlewoman, nother maiden, but as he loveth all inlike much.[2] And therefore, madam,' said Sir Bors, 'ye may say what ye will, but wit you well I will haste me to seek him and find him wheresomever he be, and God send me good tidings of him!'

And so leave we them there, and speak we of Sir Lancelot that lay in great peril. And so as this fair maiden Elaine came to Winchester she sought there all about, and by fortune Sir Lavain, her brother, was ridden to sport him to enchafe [3] his horse. And anon as this maiden Elaine saw him she knew him, and then she cried on-loud till him, and when he heard her he came to her. And anon with that she asked her brother,

'How doth my lord, Sir Lancelot?'

'Who told you, sister, that my lord's name was Sir Lancelot?'

Then she told him how Sir Gawain by his shield knew him.

So they rode together till that they came to the hermitage, and anon she alight. So Sir Lavain brought her in to Sir Lancelot, and when she saw him lie so sick and pale in his bed she might not speak, but suddenly she fell down to the earth in a swough. And there she lay a great while. And when she was relieved [4] she shrieked and said,

---

[18] with no	[2] equally
[19] kin	[3] exercise
[20] boasting	[4] recovered
[1] prevent	

'My lord, Sir Lancelot! Alas, why lie ye in this plight?'
And then she swooned again. And then Sir Lancelot prayed
Sir Lavain to take her up, 'and bring her hither to me.'

And when she came to herself Sir Lancelot lift her and
said,

'Fair maiden, why fare ye thus? For ye put me to more
pain.[5] Wherefore make ye no such cheer, for an ye be come to
comfort me ye be right welcome; and of this little hurt that
I have I shall be right hastily whole, by the grace of God.
But I marvel,' said Sir Lancelot, 'who told you my name?'

And so this maiden told him all how Sir Gawain was lodged
with her father.

'And there by your shield he discovered your name.'

'Alas,' said Sir Lancelot, 'that repenteth me[6] that my name
is known, for I am sure it will turn until anger.'[7]

And then Sir Lancelot compassed in his mind[8] that Sir
Gawain would tell Queen Guinevere how he bare the red
sleeve, and for whom, that he wist well would turn unto great
anger.[9]

So this maiden Elaine never went from Sir Lancelot, but
watched[10] him day and night, and did such attendance to him
that the French book saith there was never woman did never
more kindlier for man. Then Sir Lancelot prayed Sir Lavain
to make espies[11] in Winchester for Sir Bors if he came there,
and told him by what tokens he should know him: by a wound
in his forehead.

'For I am sure,' said Sir Lancelot, 'that Sir Bors will seek
me, for he is the same good knight that hurt me.'

Now turn we unto Sir Bors de Ganis that came until Winchester to seek after his cousin Sir Lancelot. And when he[12]
came to Winchester Sir Lavain laid watch[13] for Sir Bors.
And anon he had warning of him, and so he found him, and
anon he salewed him and told him from whence he came.

'Now, fair knight,' said Sir Bors, 'ye be welcome, and I
require you that ye will bring me to my lord Sir Lancelot.'

[5] cause me more distress
[6] I regret
[7] cause ill-feeling
[8] realised
[9] unhappiness
[10] sat by
[11] send out searchers
[12] = Sir Lavain
[13] lay in wait

'Sir,' said Sir Lavain, 'take your horse, and within this hour ye shall see him.'

So they departed and came to the hermitage. And when Sir Bors saw Sir Lancelot lie in his bed, dead pale and dis-coloured, anon Sir Bors lost his countenance, and for kindness and pity he might not speak, but wept tenderly a great while. But then when he might speak he said thus:

'Ah, my lord Sir Lancelot, God you bless, and send you hasty recovering! For full heavy am I of my misfortune and of mine unhappiness. For now I may call myself unhappy, and I dread me that God is greatly displeased with me, that He would suffer me to have such a shame for to hurt you that are all our leader and all our worship; [14] and therefore I call myself unhappy.[15] Alas, that ever such a caitiff [16] knight as I am should have power by unhappiness [17] to hurt the most noblest knight of the world! Where I so shamefully set upon you and overcharged you,[18] and where ye might have slain me, ye saved me; and so did not I, for I and all our blood did to you their utterance.[19] I marvel,' said Sir Bors, 'that my heart or my blood would serve me. Wherefore, my lord Sir Lancelot, I ask you mercy.'

'Fair cousin,' said Sir Lancelot, 'ye be right welcome; and wit you well, overmuch ye say for the pleasure of me which pleaseth me nothing,[20] for why I have the same isought; [1] for I would with pride have overcome you all. And there in my pride I was near slain, and that was in mine own default; [2] for I might have given you warning of my being there, and then had I had [3] no hurt. For it is an old-said saw, "there is hard battle thereas [4] kin and friends doth battle either against other," for there may be no mercy but mortal war. Therefore, fair cousin,' said Sir Lancelot, 'let this language overpass,[5] and all shall be welcome that God sendeth. And let us leave off this matter and speak of some rejoicing, for this that is done may

---

[14] leader of us all and the glory of our fellowship

[15] unfortunate

[16] miserable

[17] through mischance

[18] sorely pressed you

[19] their worst

[20] you say all this to please me, but it pleases me not

[1] for my intention was the same as yours

[2] that was my own fault

[3] I should have had

[4] where

[5] do not let us speak thus

not be undone; and let us find a remedy how soon that I may be [6] whole.'

Then Sir Bors leaned upon his bed's side and told Sir Lancelot how the queen was passing wroth with him, 'because ye wore the red sleeve at the great jousts.' And there Sir Bors told him all how Sir Gawain discovered it, 'by your shield that ye left with the fair maiden of Astolat.'

'Then is the queen wroth?' said Sir Lancelot. 'Therefore am I right heavy,[7] but I deserved no wrath, for all that I did was because I would not be known.'

'Sir, right so excused I you,' said Sir Bors, 'but all was in vain, for she said more largelier [8] to me than I to you say now. But, sir, is this she,' said Sir Bors, 'that is so busy about you, that men call the Fair Maiden of Astolat?'

'Forsooth, she it is,' said Sir Lancelot, 'that by no means I cannot put her from me.' [9]

'Why should ye put her from you?' said Sir Bors. 'For she is a passing fair damsel, and well beseen [10] and well taught.[11] And God would, fair cousin,' said Sir Bors, 'that ye could love her, but as to that I may not nother dare not counsel you. But I see well,' said Sir Bors, 'by her diligence about you that she loveth you entirely.' [12]

'That me repenteth,' [13] said Sir Lancelot.

'Well,' said Sir Bors, 'she is not the first that hath lost her pain [14] upon you, and that is the more pity.'

And so they talked of many more things.

And so within three or four days Sir Lancelot waxed big and light. Then Sir Bors told Sir Lancelot how there was sworn a great tournament betwixt King Arthur and the King of North Wales, that should be upon All Hallowmass Day, besides Winchester.

'Is that truth?' said Sir Lancelot. 'Then shall ye abide with me still a little while until that I be whole, for I feel myself reasonably big and strong.'

'Blessed be God!' said Sir Bors.

---

[6] that would soon make me
[7] it grieves me
[8] spoke more harshly
[9] send her away
[10] comely

[11] well-behaved
[12] with all her heart
[13] That is a pity
[14] pains

Then were they there nigh a month together, and ever this maiden Elaine did ever her diligence and labour night and day unto Sir Lancelot, that [15] there was never child nother wife more meeker till father and husband than was this fair maiden of Astolat; wherefore Sir Bors was greatly pleased with her.

So upon a day, by the assent of Sir Lavain, Sir Bors and Sir Lancelot, they made the hermit to seek in woods for divers herbs, and so Sir Lancelot made fair Elaine to gather herbs for him to make him a bain.[16] So in the meanwhile Sir Lancelot made Sir Lavain to arm him at all pieces,[17] and there he thought to essay himself upon horseback with a spear, whether he might wield his armour and his spear for his hurt or not.

And so when he was upon his horse he stirred him freshly,[18] and the horse was passing lusty and frick [19] because he was not laboured of a month before. And then Sir Lancelot bade Sir Lavain give him that great spear, and so Sir Lancelot couched that spear in the rest. The courser leapt mightily when he felt the spurs, and he that was upon him, which was the noblest horseman of the world, strained him [20] mightily and stably, and kept still the spear in the rest. And therewith Sir Lancelot strained himself so straitly,[1] with so great force, to get the courser forward, that the bottom of his wound brast [2] both within and without, and therewithal the blood came out so fiercely that he felt himself so feeble that he might not sit upon his horse. And then Sir Lancelot cried unto Sir Bors,

'Ah, Sir Bors and Sir Lavain, help! For I am come unto mine end!'

And therewith he fell down on the one side to the earth like a dead corpse. And then Sir Bors and Sir Lavain came unto him with sorrow-making out of measure. And so by fortune this maiden Elaine heard their mourning; and then she came, and when she found Sir Lancelot there armed in that place she cried and wept as she had been wood.[3] And then

---

[15] for
[16] bath
[17] fully
[18] urged him on vigorously
[19] frisky

[20] held him
[1] severely
[2] the deepest part of his wound burst
[3] mad

she kissed him and did what she might to awake him, and then she rebuked her brother and Sir Bors, and called them false traitors, and said,

'Why would ye take him out of his bed? For an he die, I will appeal you of [4] his death.'

And so with that came the hermit, Sir Baudwin of Britain, and when he found Sir Lancelot in that plight he said but little, but wit ye well he was wroth. But [5] he said, 'Let us have him in,' and anon they bore him into the hermitage and unarmed him, and laid him in his bed; and evermore his wound bled spiteously,[6] but he stirred no limb of him. Then the knight-hermit put a thing in his nose and a little deal of water in his mouth, and then Sir Lancelot waked of his swough. And then the hermit staunched his bleeding, and when Sir Lancelot might speak he [7] asked why he put his life so in jeopardy.

'Sir,' said Sir Lancelot, 'because I weened I had been strong enough, and also Sir Bors told me that there should be at Hallowmass a great jousts betwixt King Arthur and the King of North Wales. And therefore I thought to essay myself, whether I might be there or not.'

'Ah, Sir Lancelot,' said the hermit, 'your heart and your courage will never be done until your last day! But ye shall do now by my counsel: let Sir Bors depart from you, and let him do at that tournament what he may; and, by the grace of God,' said the knight-hermit, 'by that [8] the tournament be done and he comen hither again, sir, ye shall be whole, so [9] that ye will be governed by me.'

Then Sir Bors made him ready to depart from him, and Sir Lancelot said,

'Fair cousin, Sir Bors, recommend me unto all those ye ought recommend me unto, and I pray you, enforce [10] yourself at that jousts that ye may be best, for my love. And here shall I abide you, at the mercy of God, till your again-coming.' [11]

And so Sir Bors departed and came to the court of King

[4] blame you for	[8] by the time
[5] And	[9] provided
[6] copiously	[10] exert
[7] the hermit	[11] your return

Arthur, and told them in what place he left Sir Lancelot.

'That me repenteth,' [12] said the king. 'But syn he shall have his life, we all may thank God.'

And then Sir Bors told the queen what jeopardy Sir Lancelot was in when he would essayed [13] his horse:

'And all that he did was for the love of you, because he would have been at this tournament.'

'Fie on him, recreant knight!' said the queen. 'For wit you well I am right sorry an he shall have his life.'

'Madam, his life shall he have,' said Sir Bors, 'and who that would otherwise, except you, madam, we that be of his blood would help to shorten their lives! But, madam,' said Sir Bors, 'ye have been oftentimes displeased with my lord Sir Lancelot, but at all times at the end ye found him a true knight.'

And so he departed. And then every knight of the Round Table that were there that time present made them ready to that jousts at All Hallowmass. And thither drew many knights of divers countries. And as Hallowmass drew near, thither came the King of North Wales, and the King with the Hundred Knights, and Sir Galahalt the Haut Prince of Surluse. And thither came King Anguish of Ireland, and the King of Northumberland, and the King of Scots. So these three kings came to King Arthur's party.

And so that day Sir Gawain did great deeds of arms, and began first; and the heralds numbered that Sir Gawain smote down twenty knights. Then Sir Bors de Ganis came in the same time, and he was numbered that he [14] smote down twenty knights; and therefore the prize was given betwixt [15] them both, for they began first and longest endured. Also Sir Gareth, as the book saith, did that day great deeds of arms, for he smote down and pulled down thirty knights: but when he had done that deeds he tarried not but so departed, and therefore he lost his prize. And Sir Palomides did great deeds of arms that day, for he smote down twenty knights; but he departed suddenly, and men deemed that he and Sir Gareth rode together to some manner [16] adventures.

So when this tournament was done Sir Bors departed, and

[12] That is a pity
[13] wished to try
[14] it was reckoned that he

[15] divided between
[16] kind of

rode till he came to Sir Lancelot, his cousin. And then he found him walking on his feet, and there either made great joy of other.

And so he told Sir Lancelot of all the jousts, like as ye have heard.

'I marvel,' said Sir Lancelot, 'that Sir Gareth, when he had done such deeds of arms, that he would not tarry.'

'Sir, thereof we marvelled all,' said Sir Bors, 'for but if it were you, other [17] the noble knight Sir Tristram, other [17] the good knight Sir Lamorak de Galis, I saw never knight bear [18] so many knights and smite down in so little a while as did Sir Gareth. And anon as he was gone we all wist not where he became.' [19]

'By my head,' said Sir Lancelot, 'he is a noble knight, and a mighty man and well-breathed; [20] and if he were well essayed,' said Sir Lancelot, 'I would deem he were good enough for any knight that beareth the life.[1] And he is gentle, courteous and right bounteous, meek and mild, and in him is no manner of mal engine,[2] but plain, faithful, and true.'

So then they made them ready to depart from the hermitage. And so upon a morn they took their horses and this Elaine le Blanke with them. And when they came to Astolat there were they well lodged, and had great cheer of Sir Barnard, the old baron, and of Sir Tirry, his son.

And so upon the morn when Sir Lancelot should depart, fair Elaine brought her father with her, and Sir Lavain and Sir Tirry, and then thus she said:

'My lord, Sir Lancelot, now I see ye will depart from me. Now, fair knight and courteous knight,' said she, 'have mercy upon me, and suffer me not to [3] die for your love.'

'Why, what would ye that I did?' said Sir Lancelot.

'Sir, I would have you to my husband,' said Elaine.

'Fair damsel, I thank you heartily,' said Sir Lancelot, 'but truly,' said he, 'I cast me never [4] to be wedded man.'

'Then, fair knight,' said she, 'will ye be my paramour?'

'Jesu defend me!' said Sir Lancelot. 'For then I rewarded

[17] or
[18] strike
[19] went
[20] strong-winded

[1] lives
[2] guile
[3] do not let me
[4] I never intend

your father and your brother full evil for their great goodness.'

'Alas! Then,' said she, 'I must die for your love.'

'Ye shall not so,' said Sir Lancelot, 'for wit you well, fair
maiden, I might have been married an I had would,[5] but I
never applied me yet to be married. But because, fair damsel,
that ye love me as ye say ye do, I will for your good will and
kindness show to you some goodness. That is this, that wheresomever ye will beset[6] your heart upon some good knight
that will wed you, I shall give you together[7] a thousand
pound yearly, to you and to your heirs. This much will I
give you, fair maiden, for your kindness, and always while I
live to be your own knight.'

'Sir, of all this,' said the maiden, 'I will none, for but if ye
will wed me, other to be my paramour at the least, wit you
well, Sir Lancelot, my good days are done.'

'Fair damsel,' said Sir Lancelot, 'of these two things ye must
pardon[8] me.'

Then she shrieked shrilly[9] and fell down in a swough; and
then women bare her into her chamber, and there she made
overmuch sorrow. And then Sir Lancelot would[10] depart,
and there he asked Sir Lavain what he would do.

'Sir, what should I do,' said Sir Lavain, 'but follow you
but if ye drive me from you or command me to go from
you?'

Then came Sir Barnard to Sir Lancelot and said to him,

'I cannot see but that my daughter will die for your sake.'

'Sir, I may not do withal,'[11] said Sir Lancelot, 'for that me
sore repenteth. For I report me to yourself[12] that my proffer
is fair. And me repenteth,' said Sir Lancelot, 'that she loveth
me as she doth, for I was never the causer of it; for I report
me unto your son, I never early nother late proffered her
bounty nother fair behests.[13] And as for me,' said Sir Lancelot, 'I dare do that a knight should do, and say that she is a
clean maiden for me, both for deed and will. For I am right

[5] wished
[6] bestow
[7] both
[8] excuse
[9] piercingly
[10] was about to

[11] I cannot help it
[12] But you will agree
[13] your son will bear witness that
at no time did I show her regard
or make her sweet promises

heavy of her distress! For she is a full fair maiden, good and gentle, and well itaught.' [14]

'Father,' said Sir Lavain, 'I dare make good she is a clean maiden as for my lord Sir Lancelot; but she doth as I do, for sithen I saw first my lord Sir Lancelot I could never depart from him, nother nought I will, an I may [15] follow him.'

Then Sir Lancelot took his leave, and so they departed, and came to Winchester. And when King Arthur wist that Sir Lancelot was come whole and sound, the king made great joy of him; and so did Sir Gawain and all the knights of the Round Table, except Sir Agravain and Sir Mordred. Also Queen Guinevere was wood wroth [16] with Sir Lancelot, and would by no means speak with him, but estranged herself from him. And Sir Lancelot made all the means that he might [17] for to speak with the queen, but it would not be.

Now speak we of the fair maiden of Astolat that made such sorrow day and night that she never slept, ate, nother drank, and ever she made her complaint unto Sir Lancelot. So when she had thus endured a ten days, that she feebled so that she must needs pass out of this world, then she shrove her clean and received her Creator. And ever she complained still upon Sir Lancelot. Then her ghostly [18] father bade her leave such thoughts. Then she said,

'Why should I leave such thoughts? Am I not an earthly woman? And all the while the breath is in my body I may complain me, for my belief is that I do none offence, though I love an earthly man, unto God, for He formed me thereto, and all manner of good love cometh of God. And other than good love loved I never Sir Lancelot du Lake. And I take God to record, I loved never none but him, nor never shall, of earthly creature; and a clean maiden I am for him and for all other. And sithen it is the sufferance [19] of God that I shall die for so noble a knight, I beseech Thee, High Father of Heaven, have mercy upon me and my soul, and upon mine innumerable pains that I suffer may be allegeance [20] of part of my sins. For, Sweet Lord Jesu,' said the fair maiden, 'I take

---

[14] well behaved
[15] and never shall, if I am allowed to
[16] wildly angry
[17] did all he could ,
[18] spiritual
[19] will
[20] relief

God to record, I was never to Thee great offencer nother against Thy laws but that I loved this noble knight, Sir Lancelot, out of measure. And of myself, Good Lord, I had no might to withstand the fervent love, wherefore I have my death.'

And then she called her father, Sir Barnard, and her brother, Sir Tirry, and heartily she prayed her father that her brother might write a letter like as she did indite,[1] and so her father granted her. And when the letter was written word by word like as she devised it, then she prayed her father that she might be watched until she was dead. 'And while my body is hot let this letter be put in my right hand, and my hand bound fast with the letter until that I be cold. And let me be put in a fair bed with all the richest clothes that I have about me, and so let my bed and all my richest clothes be laid with me in a chariot [2] unto the next [3] place where the Thames is; and there let me be put within a barget,[4] and but one man with me, such as ye trust to steer me thither; and that my barget be covered with black samite [5] over and over. And thus, father, I beseech you let it be done.'

So her father granted it her faithfully all thing should be done like as she had devised. Then her father and her brother made great dole for her. And when this was done anon she died.

And when she was dead the corpse and the bed all was led the next way unto the Thames, and there a man and the corpse and all things as she had devised was put in the Thames. And so the man steered the barget unto Westminster, and there it rubbed and rolled to and fro a great while or any man espied it.

So by fortune King Arthur and Queen Guinevere were talking together at a window, and so as they looked into the Thames they espied that black barget and had marvel what it meant. Then the king called Sir Kay, and showed it him.

'Sir,' said Sir Kay, 'wit you well, there is some new tidings.'

'Therefore go ye thither,' said the king to Sir Kay, 'and take with you Sir Braundiles and Sir Agravain, and bring me ready word what is there.'

1 as she would direct
2 cart
3 nearest
4 small boat
5 rich silk

Then these three knights departed and came to the barget and went in. There they found the fairest corpse lying in a rich bed that ever ye saw, and a poor man sitting in the barget's end, and no word would he speak. So these three knights returned unto the king again, and told him what they found.

'That fair corpse will I see,' said the king.

And so the king took the queen by the hand and went thither. Then the king made the barget to be held fast, and then the king and the queen went in with certain knights with them, and there he saw the fairest woman lie in a rich bed, covered unto her middle [6] with many rich clothes,[7] and all was of cloth of gold. And she lay as she had smiled.

Then the queen espied the letter in her right hand and told the king. Then the king took it and said,

'Now am I sure this letter will tell us what she was, and why she is come hither.'

So then the king and the queen went out of the barget, and so commanded a certain [8] to wait [9] upon the barget. And so when the king was come to his chamber he called many knights about [10] him, and said that he would wit openly [11] what was written within that letter. Then the king brake it, and made a clerk to read it, and this was the intent [12] of the letter.

'Most noble knight, my lord Sir Lancelot, now hath death made us two at debate [13] for your love. And I was your lover, that men called the Fair Maiden of Astolat. Therefore unto all ladies I make my moan,[14] yet for my soul ye pray and bury me at the least and offer ye my mass-penny: this is my last request. And a clean maiden I died, I take God to witness. And pray for my soul, Sir Lancelot, as thou [15] art peerless.'

This was all the substance in the letter. And when it was read, the king, the queen and all the knights wept for pity of the doleful complaints. Then was Sir Lancelot sent for, and when he was come King Arthur made the letter to be read to him. And when Sir Lancelot heard it word by word, he said,

---

[6] waist
[7] coverings
[8] someone
[9] keep watch
[10] to
[11] wished to hear in their presence
[12] content
[13] divided us
[14] lament
[15] thou who

'My lord Arthur, wit ye well I am right heavy of the death of this fair lady. And God knoweth I was never causer of her death by my willing, and that will I report me unto [16] her own brother that here he is, Sir Lavain. I will not say nay,' said Sir Lancelot, 'but that she was both fair and good, and much I was beholden unto her, but she loved me out of measure.'

'Sir,' said the queen, 'ye might have showed her some bounty [17] and gentleness which might have preserved her life.'

'Madam,' said Sir Lancelot, 'she would none otherways be answered but that she would be my wife other else my paramour, and of these two I would not grant her. But I proffered her, for her good love that she showed me, a thousand pound yearly to her and to her heirs, and to wed any manner of knight that she could find best to love in her heart. For, madam,' said Sir Lancelot, 'I love not to be constrained to love, for love must only arise of the heartself, and not by none constraint.'

'That is truth, sir,' said the king, 'and with many knights, love is free in himself, and never will be bound; for where he is bounden he looseth himself.' Then said the king unto Sir Lancelot, 'Sir, it will be your worship that ye oversee [18] that she be interred worshipfully.' [19]

'Sir,' said Sir Lancelot, 'that shall be done as I can best devise.'

And so many knights yode thither to behold that fair dead maiden, and so upon the morn she was interred richly. And Sir Lancelot offered her mass-penny; [20] and all those knights of the Table Round that were there at that time offered with Sir Lancelot. And then the poor man went again [1] with the barget.

Then the queen sent for Sir Lancelot and prayed him of mercy for why that she had been wroth with him causeless. [2]

'This is not the first time,' said Sir Lancelot, 'that ye have

[16] as to that I call to witness
[17] favour
[18] take care
[19] with honour
[20] mass-penny: *an offering of money made at mass*

[1] back
[2] prayed him to forgive her for having been unjustly displeased with him

been displeased with me causeless. But, madam, ever I must suffer you,[3] but what sorrow that I endure, ye take no force.' [4]

So this passed on all that winter, with all manner of hunting and hawking, and jousts and tourneys were many betwixt many great lords.

. . . I PRAY YOU ALL GENTLEMEN AND GENTLEWOMEN THAT READETH THIS BOOK OF ARTHUR AND HIS KNIGHTS FROM THE BEGINNING TO THE ENDING [5] PRAY FOR ME WHILE I AM ON LIVE THAT GOD SEND ME GOOD DELIVERANCE.[6] AND WHEN I AM DEAD I PRAY YOU ALL PRAY FOR MY SOUL. FOR THIS BOOK WAS ENDED THE NINTH YEAR OF THE REIGN OF KING EDWARD THE FOURTH BY SIR THOMAS MALEORÉ, KNIGHT, AS JESU HELP HIM FOR HIS GREAT MIGHT, AS HE IS THE SERVANT OF JESU BOTH DAY AND NIGHT.

[3] bear with you
[4] it matters not to you
[5] *This passage occurs at the very end of Malory's last romance,* The Tale of the Death of King Arthur, *but the words* this book of Arthur and his knights *refer to the entire collection of romances.*
[6] that God may liberate me from imprisonment

BIBLIOGRAPHICAL NOTE

All the editions of Malory's works produced before 1947 were based directly or indirectly on the folio volume published by William Caxton under the title of *Le Morte Darthur* 'in the abbey of Westminster, the last day of July, the year of Our Lord MCCCCLXXXV.' Two copies of this volume are extant; one, which is complete but for the fly-leaf, is in the Pierpont Morgan Library in New York, the other, wanting eleven leaves, in the John Rylands Library in Manchester. The text was reprinted with some alterations by Wynkyn de Worde in 1498. No fewer than three editions, including a reprint of Wynkyn de Worde's (1529), appeared in the sixteenth century and one in the seventeenth (William Stansby's, 1634). Of the numerous modern editions the most important are Southey's (1817), Thomas Wright's (1856 and 1866), Edward Strachey's (1868), H. Oskar Sommer's (in three volumes, 1889–91), and A. W. Pollard's (Macmillan, 1900, 1903, and 1927).

In 1934 a manuscript of Malory's romances was discovered in the Fellows' Library of Winchester College by the then Librarian (now Rector of Lincoln College, Oxford) Mr. W. F. Oakeshott, and in 1947 a three-volume edition based on that manuscript was produced by the Clarendon Press. It seems reasonably certain that the Winchester manuscript and Caxton's *Le Morte Darthur* represent two collateral versions of Malory's text, although Caxton clearly took more liberties with it than did the scribes to whom we owe the manuscript.

The discovery of the manuscript version confirmed some of the conclusions previously reached with regard to the author's identity. The first to identify him was G. L. Kittredge in a study entitled *Who Was Sir Thomas Malory?* (Boston, 1897; reprinted from *Studies and Notes in Philology and Literature*, Vol. V). Subsequent biographical studies include: E. K. Chambers, *Sir Thomas Malory* (English Association, Pamphlet No. 51), London, 1922 (reprinted in *Sir Thomas Wyatt and other*

Collected Studies, London, 1933); Edward Hicks, *Sir Thomas Malory, His Turbulent Career*, Harvard University Press, 1928; chapter I of my *Malory*, Oxford, 1929; and A. C. Baugh, 'Documenting Sir Thomas Malory,' *Speculum*, Vol. VIII (1933).

Sir Thomas Malory (or Malleoré) is the author of eight Arthurian romances forming what he describes as 'the book of Arthur and his knights' (the title *Le Morte Darthur* is in fact that of his last romance — the *Morte Arthur* — applied by Caxton, with little justification, to the entire collection). The first to be written was an adaptation of the English alliterative *Morte Arthur* (*The Noble Tale of King Arthur and the Emperor Lucius*). This was followed by six romances based on French models (the 'French books,' as Malory calls them), viz. *The Tale of King Arthur, The Noble Tale of Sir Lancelot, The Book of Sir Gareth, The Book of Sir Tristram, The Quest of the Holy Grail*, and *The Book of Sir Lancelot and Queen Guinevere*. For his last romance — *The Tale of the Death of King Arthur* or *The Morte Arthur Saunz Guerdon* — he used, in addition to a French romance, the English stanzaic *Le Morte Arthur*.

The discovery of the 'books' he had at his disposal has been a slow and difficult process. One of his major sources is still unknown — that of *The Book of Sir Gareth;* some are still unpublished, and comparatively few are available in reliable modern editions. But so far as the present selection is concerned, the only work which presents any serious difficulty is *The Knight of the Cart*. The story was originally part of a twelfth-century French poem by Chrétien de Troyes (*Li conte de la charrete*). Malory's immediate source, not adequately represented in any known text, must have been a prose work of the thirteenth century closely related to the French prose romance of Lancelot (*Le Roman en prose de Lancelot: le conte de la charrette*, ed. Gweneth Hutchings, Paris, 1928). The work has no connection with the 'Book' in which it occurs — *The Book of Sir Lancelot and Queen Guinevere* — and it seemed justifiable, therefore, to transfer it to its normal chronological place. The next section — *Lancelot and Elaine* — is based on a text which is extant, but of which there is no satisfactory edition. Malory seems to have used a manuscript of the *Tristan* similar to MS. Bibl. Nat. fr. 99 (ff. 508 verso–548 recto) and somewhat different from the one published by H. O. Sommer in *Modern Philology*, Vol. V (pp. 55–84; 181–200, and 291–341) under the title of *Galahad and Perceval*.

Merlin, Balin, and *Pelleas and Ettard* are adaptations of parts of a thirteenth-century cyclic romance generally known as *La Suite du Merlin* and preserved in two manuscripts: British Museum Add. 38117 and Cambridge University Library Add. 7071. The latter, discovered in 1945, is still unpublished. The text of the British Museum manuscript was edited by Gaston Paris and Jacob Ulrich in 1886 under the title of *Merlin.* There is also a separate recent edition of the portion corresponding to Malory's *Balin* (*Le Roman de Balain* edited by M. D. Legge, Manchester, 1942).

The Holy Grail is an extract from Malory's *Quest of the Holy Grail* which is substantially an abridged translation of the Grail branch of the French Arthurian Cycle. There are three modern editions of the French text: F. J. Furnivall's (Roxburghe Club, 1864), H. O. Sommer's (*The Vulgate Version of the Arthurian Romances*, Vol. VI, 1913), and Albert Pauphilet's (*La Queste del Saint Graal*, Paris, 1933), by far the most reliable of the three.

The last two sections — *The Poisoned Apple* and *The Fair Maid of Astolat* — belong, like *The Knight of the Cart,* to Malory's last romance but one, *The Book of Sir Lancelot and Queen Guinevere,* based mainly upon the final branch of the French Arthurian Cycle (*Mort Artu* or *La Mort le roi Artu*). This branch has been published four times (by J. D. Bruce in 1910, by H. O. Sommer in *The Vulgate Version of the Arthurian Romances* in 1913, and by M. Jean Frappier in 1936 and again in 1955), but the only critical editions are the last two. The portions corresponding to Malory's two stories occur at the beginning of the French text (pp. 1–84 of the 1936 edition), interwoven with each other and interspersed with other material.

The following studies have a special bearing on the tales included in the present volume:

Chambers, E. K., *Sir Thomas Wyatt and Some Collected Studies,* London, 1933, pp. 21–45.

———— *English Literature at the Close of the Middle Ages,* Oxford, 1945, pp. 185–205,

Ferrier, Janet M., *Forerunners of the French Novel,* Manchester, 1954, pp. 7–21.

Hibbard, Laura A., 'Malory's Book of Balin' (in *Mediaeval Studies in Memory of Gertrude Schoepperle Loomis,* Paris and New York, 1927, pp. 175–195).

MacNeice, Louis, 'Sir Thomas Malory' (in *The English Novelists: A Survey of the Novel by Twenty Contemporary Novelists,* edited by Derek Verschoyle, London, 1926), pp. 19–28.

Scudder, Vida D., *Le Morte Darthur of Sir Thomas Malory: A Study of the Book and Its Sources,* London and New York, 1921, pp. 195–200 and 259–328.

Vettermann, Ella, *Die Balen-Dichtungen und Ihre Quellen,* Halle a. S., 1918, pp. 52–84.

Vinaver, Eugène (ed.), *The Works of Sir Thomas Malory,* Oxford 1947, pp. 1281–5, 1299–1318, 1351–6, 1511–8, 1568–71 and 1572–96.

Whitehead, F., 'On Certain Episodes in the Fourth Book of Malory's "Morte Darthur," ' *Medium Ævum,* Vol. II (October 1933), pp. 199–216.

RIVERSIDE EDITIONS

* In preparation